Y10

SAL

SCIENCE

GCSE Volume 1
Year 10 Units

Contents

About this book

Salters GCSE Science has been written for your GCSE course. Teachers and examiners have written the book to help you learn about science and prepare for your exams.

We hope that you will enjoy using the books, learning about science and how it affects you.

To help you find your way around the book it has been divided into 11 units.

Each unit starts with an introductory page. Read this page to get a feel for some of the things you will be learning about in the unit. There are also some questions to try before you start so that you can find out how much you already know.

Double-page spreads

The material you need to study has been divided up into double-page spreads to help you find your way around. Here are some of the things you will come across on the double-page spreads:

Words in bold type are important scientific words. Make sure that you understand what they mean. You may find that it helps to make a list of these words when you come to revise.

Things to do box

Things to do

When you come across a box like this it will contain questions or other tasks for you to complete. Answering questions will help you to check your understanding.

Fact box

A box like this will contain important scientific facts. Make sure that you know and understand everything that appears in these boxes.

Higher tier box

Material in a box like this will only be tested in the higher tier exams. Check with your teacher to find out which exam you are entered for.

Student sheet symbol

This symbol means that you may be asked to do an activity or worksheet to help with your study. Your teacher will decide which sheets you will need.

At the end of each unit you will find plenty of questions to test what you have understood. These questions are similar to the type of questions that you may be asked in your exams. Remember, practice makes perfect.

We hope you enjoy using the books.

The Salters GCSE science team.

INTRODUCING
Energy matters

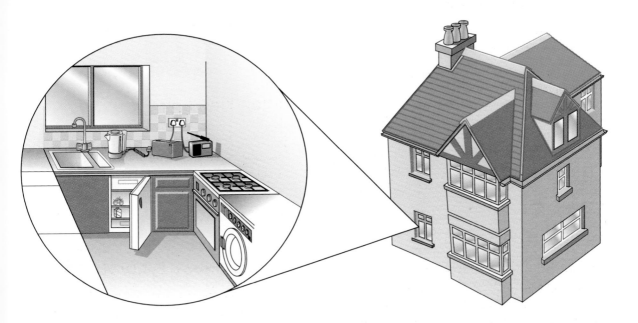

n our homes, we use many labour-saving devices to do jobs for us. They all need energy to work.

ry these first

Which one of these is a renewable source of energy for generating electricity?

coal   oil   sunlight   uranium

Which one of these is the ultimate source of most of Earth's energy?

Arabia   Milky Way   Moon   Sun

Which one of these flows from areas at high temperature to areas at low temperature?

force   heat   pressure   water

Heat energy can move through different things by conduction, convection or radiation. Which method is important in each of these?

a The handle of a saucepan gets hot.

b Energy from the Sun reaches Earth.

c Warmth from a radiator spreads round a room.

25 J of electrical energy is transferred to a light bulb. Which of these is the amount of light energy transferred out?

5 J   25 J   50 J

In this unit you will learn:

- that *energy* has many forms - electrical, chemical, light, strain, heat, sound, kinetic, gravitational

- that to make things happen (to do *work*), energy must be transferred from one form to another

- that *power* (measured in watts) is the rate of transfer of energy

- that the *power rating* of a piece of electrical equipment shows how fast it transfers energy, and so how much it will cost to use it

- that it is not usually possible to transfer all the energy supplied to a device into the form you want - some gets spread out into less useful forms

- that *efficiency* is the percentage of input energy that does something useful

- how insulation can slow down the rate at which energy flows out of buildings

- that the U-value of an insulator allows you to calculate the rate of heat energy transfer.

1 Energy gets the jobs done

Energy slaves work for us!

It is often said that we do not work as hard now as people did two hundred years ago. This is quite true! New discoveries have taught us how to build devices that act like slaves and do jobs for us. Here are some examples.

 The word work has a special meaning in science. Work is done when energy is transferred from one form to another.

The amount of work done is a measure of the amount of energy transferred usefully.

We use all kinds of labour-saving devices that do work for us.

Things to do

1   Each of the devices shown on this page needs to be supplied with energy to make it work. Write a list of the devices and, for each one, write how the energy is supplied. Look around you at home or at school and to add other devices to your list.

2   As each of the devices is working, it takes in a supply of energy and transfers it into a different form. Go down your list and write down, for each device, what form of energy it is designed to produce (for example, an electric drill turns electrical energy into movement energy).

Energy in and energy out

Each device needs a supply of energy. While it is working it transfers energy to some other form. Energy does not magically appear from nowhere, and it doesn't disappear completely.

 Energy cannot be created or destroyed it is simply converted from one form to another. This is called the principle of **conservation of energy**.

Arrow diagrams show the balance of 'energy in' and 'energy out' for a working device.

The arrow on the left, pointing towards the device, shows how energy is transferred into it. The arrow on the right, pointing away from the device, shows the form of energy produced.

Fuels: concentrated sources of energy

Some of the devices in the picture opposite make use of chemical energy stored in fuels. When fuels are burned, heat energy is produced. This heat is used directly in the gas stove for cooking, and turned into other forms of energy in devices like the lawn-mower.

Fossil fuels (coal, oil and natural gas) have been formed very slowly over millions of years from the remains of dead plants and animals. Once used, they cannot be replaced. They are called **non-renewable fuels**.

Wood is used as a fuel in many parts of the world. Trees can be replaced in a few years, so wood is called a **renewable** energy resource. Of course, if too many trees are cut down too quickly, the supply will run out. Carefully planned schemes of cutting and replanting are needed to ensure a continuous supply. This is an example of **sustainable development**.

Energy resources that can be obtained straight from nature are called **primary energy resources**.

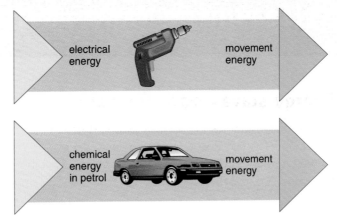

These arrow diagrams show the energy inputs and outputs for some common devices.

Electricity – a secondary energy source

Many primary sources of energy are not easy to transport. You cannot easily take a sack of coal wherever you go, and even the wind does not always blow in the right places!

It is often much easier to supply energy electrically. Almost every corner of the UK is supplied by the National Grid of electricity cables. Electricity is called a **secondary energy source**, because it is made by using some other, primary energy resource such as coal, gas and wind.

Batteries provide a completely portable source of small amounts of electricity, by transferring the chemical energy of substances inside.

We burn fuels to produce energy, which we use in all kinds of devices from steam engines to stoves.

A clear-felled area in Washington, USA.

> **?**
>
> ## Things to do
>
> 3   Make a list of all the types of fuel you know about. Which are renewable?
>
> 4   Look at your list of 'energy slave' devices from the previous page. Which ones are supplied with electrical energy? Do they use batteries, or 'mains' electricity?

2 Measuring (and paying for) energy

Units for energy

Energy is measured in units called **joules**. One joule (1 J) is not very much energy, so we often use larger units like the **kilojoule** (kJ) and the **megajoule** (MJ).

1 kJ = 1000 J

1 MJ = 1 000 000 J

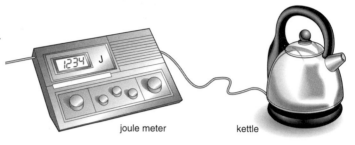

joule meter   kettle

So how big is a joule? These examples may give you an idea.

A joule meter can be used to measure how much electrical energy is transferred into a kettle of water.

- Raising a bag of sugar from the floor to a height just above your head gives it about 20 J of gravitational energy.
- You have about 3 kJ of kinetic energy when you run at full speed.
- About 50 kJ of heat energy is needed to make a cup of coffee.
- A chocolate bar may provide 5 MJ of energy when you eat it!

You need to be able to swap from one unit to another. For example, how many joules do you need to make a cup of coffee?

50 kJ = 50 × 1000 = 50 000 J

Power ratings (SS) EM1

All the devices you have studied do their work by transferring **energy**. The amount of **work** done is a measure of how much energy has been transferred.

Power is the rate of doing work – it measures how fast energy is being transferred. The unit for power is the **watt** (W). A power of 1 watt means one joule of energy is transferred each second.

1 W = 1 J/s

Many devices that are supplied with electrical energy have a **power rating**. This tells you how quickly energy is transferred through them. The watt is a small unit. Larger multiples are often used.

1 kilowatt (kW) = 1000 watts (W)

A kettle may have a power of 3 kW. If it is switched on for one minute, the electrical energy transferred to it is easily calculated.

Each device has its power rating shown.

energy = power × time = 3000 W × 60 s = 180 000 J

Of course, energy costs money. So the higher the power rating, the more it will cost to run a device.

Counting the cost of electricity

Household electricity meters measure the amount of electrical energy delivered to your home. The unit used, the kilowatt-hour (kWh), is chosen to be a sensible size, compared to the amount of energy transferred by mains electrical equipment.

Electricity bills show the number of **units** used. The unit is 1 kWh. The bill also shows the cost per unit.

The bill will also include a 'standing charge', which is to pay for the service and use of the meter.

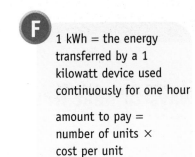

F 1 kWh = the energy transferred by a 1 kilowatt device used continuously for one hour

amount to pay = number of units × cost per unit

Which devices are most expensive to run?

The power rating of a device tells you how expensive it will be in use. This table shows some typical values.

Device	Power (kW)	Power (W)
oven	5	5000
cooker ring	1	1000
immersion heater	3	3000
iron	1	1000
one-bar fire	1	1000
television	0.3	300
light	0.1	100

Patterns in electricity demand

The demand for electricity varies throughout the day. This is a problem for the managers of power stations. They need to plan carefully to avoid wasting fuel at quiet times, but be able to satisfy demand at busy times.

Things to do

1 Here is a table showing the devices switched on in one family's home during part of an evening. Using the power rating table on this page, work out the total demand for electricity in each quarter of an hour, in kilowatts, and draw a bar chart to show your results.

Time (pm)	Devices switched on
5.30–5.45	oven, 4 lights
6.00–6.15	oven, 2 cooker rings, 4 lights, TV
6.15–6.30	2 lights, one-bar fire
6.30–6.45	3 lights, immersion heater, one-bar fire
6.45–7.00	3 lights, immersion heater, one-bar fire
7.15–7.30	2 lights, one-bar fire, TV, iron
7.30–7.45	2 lights, one-bar fire, TV

2 Using your results for the demand in kilowatts during each period, work out the energy used, in kilowatt-hours (remember each period is a quarter of an hour).

3 If each unit (kWh) of electricity costs 10p, how much is the cost of the electricity to the family for the time between 5.30 and 7.45 pm on the evening described?

4 Work out an energy demand profile like this for your own home!

Ways to heat water (SS) EM2

If you want to heat up some water, you could do it in a saucepan on top of the cooker, or in an electric kettle. Does it make any difference which way you do it? If you use the same amount of water and the same temperature change, the same amount of energy will go into the water in either case.

You will find that the kettle method uses less electrical energy than the saucepan. Why is this? The total amount of energy at the end of the process must be the same as at the beginning. So, if the saucepan method needs extra energy, where has it gone to?

The answer is that some of the energy has escaped round the sides of the saucepan to heat up the air! Not all of the energy has gone where you wanted it to go. We can show this using energy arrow diagrams.

When you heat water using a saucepan, the energy in is the same as the total energy out, but not all of it has gone where you wanted it to go!

Where does the energy go to?

The pictures show some other examples of energy going where you don't want it to!

Energy efficiency

When energy is transferred, it is almost always the case that not all of it goes where you want it to go. That is, not all the energy is transferred into a useful form.

The **efficiency** of a device is a measure of how much of the energy transferred goes to do useful work.

$$\text{efficiency} = \frac{\text{useful energy out}}{\text{total energy put in}} \times 100\%$$

So, the most perfect machine would be 100% efficient.

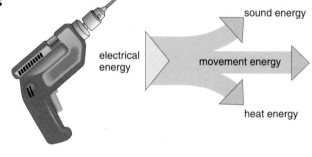

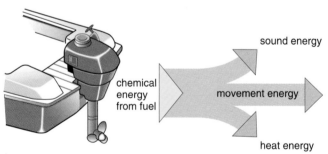

Whenever energy is transferred, some is almost always transferred into forms that are not useful.

More light in dark places

An ordinary 100 W filament light bulb produces about 15 W of light energy – the rest is lost as heat. The bulb has an efficiency of 15%.

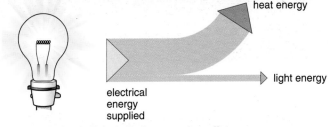

Ordinary electric light bulbs have very low efficiency.

A fluorescent tube that produces the same amount of light (15 W) uses only 18 W of electrical energy.

> The fluorescent light is
> $$\frac{15}{18} \times 100\% = 83\% \text{ efficient}$$

Using fluorescent lights instead of filament lights means paying for less electricity while still getting the same amount of light! Also, if less electricity is used, then less fuel needs to be burned in power stations.

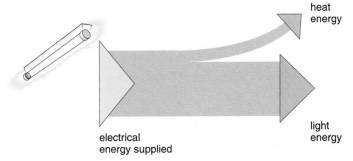

Fluorescent tube lights are far more efficient – a smaller proportion of the energy put in is wasted as heat.

Energy spreads out (SS) EM3

If you look at all the examples on these two pages, you will see that some of the energy put in is always transferred to heat. It is because of this that lots of devices get hot while they are working. However, after they are switched off, they cool down again – where has the energy gone?

Heat flows from hot objects to cooler surroundings, so it spreads out into the surroundings. The heat energy that is spread out is very difficult to make any use of – it is effectively lost, or wasted.

One way to 'save' energy is to avoid unnecessary activities. Another is to make each activity as efficient as possible.

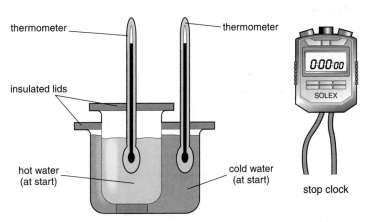

Heat energy spreads from the hot water in the small beaker to the cold water in the large beaker.

?

Things to do

1   Draw arrow diagrams for these energy transfers. You will need to do some calculations.

 a   A candle transfers 200 J of chemical energy into 50 J of light energy and some heat energy.

 b   Electrical energy transferred in a motor becomes 50 J of kinetic energy, 10 J of sound energy and 20 J of heat energy.

4 Keeping heat in your house

In the UK, we live in a cold climate. Large amounts of energy are used to keep buildings comfortably warm, and these can be very expensive.

Heat and temperature

Heat energy and temperature are not the same thing, but people often get them confused. Heat energy is measured in joules; temperature is measured in °C (with a thermometer).

> Heat energy flows from areas at high temperature to areas at lower temperature.

Replacing heat

To keep the temperature of a house constant, the heat energy that flows out must be replaced. There are several ways in which this can be done:

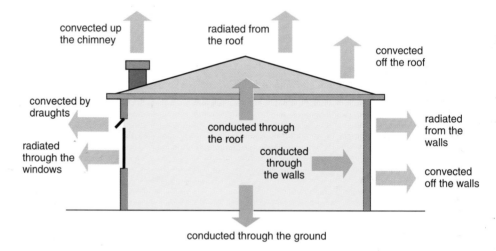

Heat energy is transferred out of a hot house in many different ways. These heat energy flows can be reduced by careful design, but not stopped completely. Any reduction in the rates of these energy flows saves money, because it saves on the fuel or electricity needed to keep the house at a steady warm temperature.

- burning coal, natural gas, wood, oil
- using electric heaters
- capturing heat from the Sun.

Whatever method is employed, cutting down the rate of heat loss saves money.

Radiation

Heat energy can flow from one place to another as **infrared radiation**. This is a wave, similar to light, but with a longer wavelength.

- Hot objects emit much more radiation than cold ones.
- Reflecting surfaces emit much less radiation than dull ones.
- Dull surfaces absorb much more radiation than reflecting ones.
- Infrared radiation passes through empty space and transparent materials (such as glass).

Convection

Heat energy from the building flows into the cold air next to the roof and walls. As the air heats up, it expands, and its density falls. The warmed air floats upwards. Of course, as the air moves away, it takes the heat energy with it. The heat energy is **convected** away.

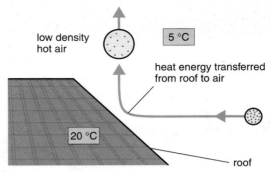

This is natural convection. Wind blows hot air away from the roof. Building your house in a sheltered place can save a lot of energy.

Conduction

There is only one way in which heat energy can flow through a solid – by **conduction**.

All solids, liquids and gases are made up of particles. As heat flows into a substance, its particles vibrate more and more vigorously. It is this greater movement of particles that makes liquids and gases expand when they are heated – the particles move further away from each other.

The particles in a solid can't move away from their positions. So as you heat up a solid, its particles just vibrate more violently.

This is how conduction works in solids.

- Heat energy arrives at the hot surface.
- The particles in the top layer vibrate more vigorously.
- These particles hit other particles below, making *them* vibrate more violently.
- So the energy is passed from particle to particle, through the solid.

Liquids and gases can also conduct heat energy, but because their particles are further apart, it takes longer for the energy to be transferred through them.

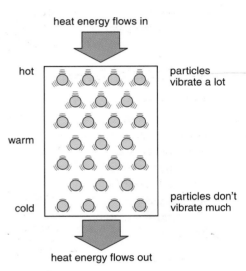

Heat is conducted through a solid as the particles knock into one another and so pass on their energy. Metals are much better conductors than other solids.

Evaporation

When a liquid **evaporates**, it turns to a gas. It takes energy to make a liquid evaporate. This is because particles in a gas have more energy than particles in a liquid. Houses in hot climates often use evaporating water to keep them cool.

Things to do

1. How does heat get to sausages when they are cooked under a hot grill?
2. In most ovens, why is the top shelf the hottest one?
3. Saucepans often have metal bodies and plastic handles. Why?
4. Why is the cooling element of a freezer at the top of the compartment?
5. Why are the cooling fins at the back of a refrigerator always painted black?

5 Cutting energy costs

Insulating your home

Each year we use a vast amount of energy to heat our homes. The cost of this energy is about £10 billion a year in the UK. How can we reduce this?

Some of the energy used in heating homes is wasted. One way of cutting waste is to use **insulation**. Of course, insulation itself costs money to install.

Things to do

Use information from the diagram to answer these questions.

1   Draw up a table listing the cost of each type of insulation, and how much it would save in a year.

2   Work out how long it would take to recover the cost of each type of insulation from the savings made. This is called the 'pay-back time'.

3   List the types of insulation in order of cost effectiveness.

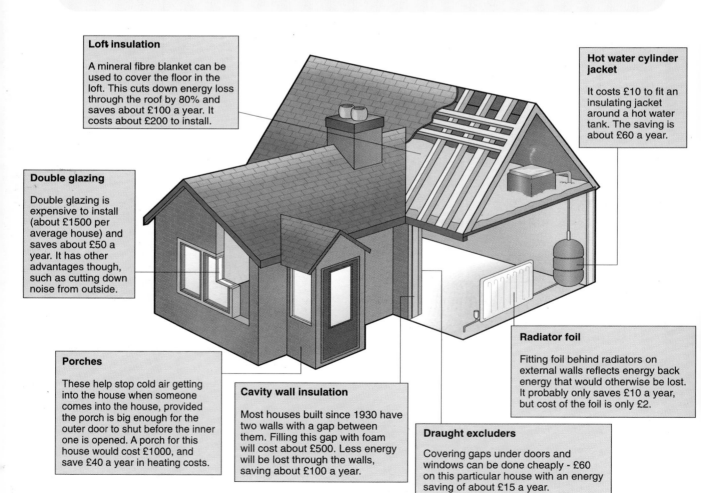

Loft insulation

A mineral fibre blanket can be used to cover the floor in the loft. This cuts down energy loss through the roof by 80% and saves about £100 a year. It costs about £200 to install.

Hot water cylinder jacket

It costs £10 to fit an insulating jacket around a hot water tank. The saving is about £60 a year.

Double glazing

Double glazing is expensive to install (about £1500 per average house) and saves about £50 a year. It has other advantages though, such as cutting down noise from outside.

Porches

These help stop cold air getting into the house when someone comes into the house, provided the porch is big enough for the outer door to shut before the inner one is opened. A porch for this house would cost £1000, and save £40 a year in heating costs.

Cavity wall insulation

Most houses built since 1930 have two walls with a gap between them. Filling this gap with foam will cost about £500. Less energy will be lost through the walls, saving about £100 a year.

Draught excluders

Covering gaps under doors and windows can be done cheaply - £60 on this particular house with an energy saving of about £15 a year.

Radiator foil

Fitting foil behind radiators on external walls reflects energy back energy that would otherwise be lost. It probably only saves £10 a year, but cost of the foil is only £2.

This diagram shows the different kinds of insulation available, how much they cost and how much they save.

Insulating yourself

Air is a very good insulator. It doesn't let heat energy flow through it easily. However, air convects heat energy very easily. Insulating materials are fluffy, with lots of tiny holes to trap air and stop it moving. Trapped air cannot convect the heat energy away.

The chemical reactions that keep us alive work best if our body is at 37 °C. Our surroundings are usually at a much lower temperature, so heat energy flows out of us all the time. We all generate heat energy, as we combine glucose with oxygen in our cells. Wrapping ourselves up in layers of fluffy material (clothes) cuts down the rate of heat loss, keeping our temperature at a safe value.

Clothes can stop heat energy getting to you. This firefighter has shiny clothes which reflect infrared radiation from the fire.

U-values (SS) EM6

Architects use U-values to work out how fast buildings will lose heat in winter, so that they can design adequate heating. The U-value of a material tells you how effective it is as an insulator.
A small U-value means the material is a good insulator.

Material	U-value (W per m² per °C)
cavity wall	0.75
insulated cavity wall	0.50
uninsulated roof	2.00
roof with 15 cm insulation	0.25
single glazed windows	5.00
double glazed window	3.00

A house has 40 m² of double glazed windows. The inside is at 20 °C, and the outside at 5 °C. At what rate does heat energy flow out of the house through the windows?

heat loss = U-value × area × temperature difference

heat loss = 3.0 × 40 × (20 − 5) = 1800 W or 1.8 kW

Take another look at the heat loss equation above. Notice how cutting down the temperature difference will also reduce the rate at which heat energy escapes. So turning down the thermostat is the simplest way to save money on heating a house!

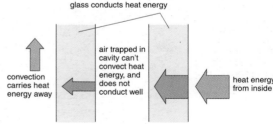

Air trapped in double glazing or cavity walls makes a very effective insulator.

? Things to do

4 Estimate the areas of the walls, windows and ceiling of your classroom. Use the U-values in the table above to estimate the rate of heat loss when the temperature outside is 10 °C lower than inside.

Look around carefully and you may see houses with solar panels on their roofs. These panels transfer (free!) light energy from the Sun to heat energy in water.

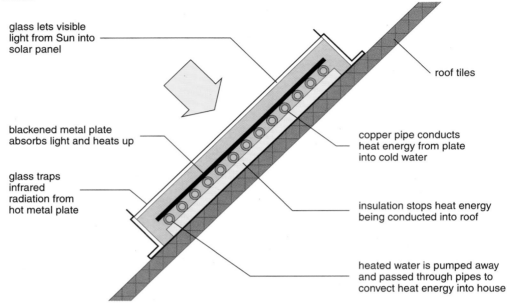

glass lets visible light from Sun into solar panel

roof tiles

blackened metal plate absorbs light and heats up

copper pipe conducts heat energy from plate into cold water

glass traps infrared radiation from hot metal plate

insulation stops heat energy being conducted into roof

heated water is pumped away and passed through pipes to convect heat energy into house

Light energy from the Sun is transferred to heat energy in the water pipes. The heated water is then piped around the house to heat the rooms by convection.

Solar heating (SS) EM7

Notice how the solar panel uses glass to trap heat energy. The glass lets **short wavelength** light into the panel, but won't let **long wavelength** infrared radiation *escape* again. So the temperature inside the panel can be much higher than outside.

Solar cells

Solar panels are not the only way of transferring light energy from the Sun into something useful. Solar cells transfer sunlight directly into electrical energy. This efficiency is much lower than for a solar heating panel, but electrical energy is more useful than heat energy.

- It can be transferred long distances along wires.
- It can be transferred into a wide variety of other forms of energy.
- It can be stored as chemical energy in batteries.

Electricity is a form of energy that is relatively easy to transport over long distances.

The 'greenhouse effect'

Greenhouses trap energy to keep plants warm in the same way. Short wavelength light from the Sun enters through the glass, and causes objects inside to warm up. These warm objects then emit long wavelength infrared radiation, but this cannot escape back out through the glass – so more and more heat energy is collected inside, and the temperature gradually rises.

You don't need glass to trap infrared radiation. Some gases (such as carbon dioxide and methane) make very good reflectors of heat radiation. Just like the glass over a solar panel, they trap the longer wavelength infrared radiation given off from the Earth's surface. Without this 'greenhouse effect', the Earth would be too cold to support life. However, human activities such as burning fossil fuels, which increase carbon dioxide levels in the atmosphere, may result in **global warming**, leading to:

- rising temperatures on the Earth's surface
- melting of glaciers and polar ice caps raising sea levels
- changing climate.

Stored sunshine

Much of our electricity comes from **non-renewable** energy sources:

- oil   - natural gas   - coal   - uranium.

The first three in the list above are known as **fossil fuels**. They contain chemical energy from plants and animals that lived millions of years ago.

Uranium is the fuel for nuclear power stations. Like other heavy elements in the Earth, it was formed billions of years ago as large heavy stars exploded when they ran out of atoms to fuse together.

Using non-renewable energy sources to generate electricity makes a lot of polluting waste.

- Fossil fuels need to be burned in air to transfer their chemical energy into heat energy. This produces carbon dioxide, a greenhouse gas.
- Oil often contains sulphur. When burned, this produces sulphur dioxide, which can react with water in the atmosphere to create acid rain.
- The spent fuel from nuclear power stations is radioactive. It needs to be stored extremely carefully.

Renewable energy resources

There are a number of **renewable** energy sources that can be used to make electricity. They don't generate any pollution and they can't run out of energy:

- **wind power** varies from hour to hour and needs many wind turbines
- **tidal power** is expensive to set up, and only works for part of each day
- **solar cells** cost a lot to install and need to cover a large area of land
- the technology for **wave power** is still being developed.

?

Things to do

1 A closed car gets hot inside when left in the Sun. Explain why this happens.
2 List the advantages and disadvantages of using solar cells to make electricity.
3 Describe the difference between a renewable and a non-renewable energy source.
4 Explain the disadvantages of generating electricity from fossil fuels.
5 Design a poster that encourages people to use electricity from renewable energy sources.

1   What is the name of the energy being transferred to the underlined objects?

   a   A <u>girder</u> being lifted up by a crane.

   b   A <u>ball</u> being thrown sideways.

   c   A <u>girl</u> eating a cake.

   d   A <u>TV</u> is plugged into the mains supply.

   e   A boy shouts at his <u>mum</u>.

   f   A lamp is switched on in a <u>room</u>.

2   Take a look at your kitchen. Make a list of all the devices which use energy. Say what they do. State the type of energy transferred into them.

3   Draw energy transfer diagrams for each of these.

   a   A catapult is used to fling some mud.

   b   A ball is thrown up into the air and falls to the ground.

   c   A girl runs uphill at a steady speed.

   d   A TV is switched on.

   e   A car accelerates along a level road.

4   Complete the gaps.
    Choose words from the list.

   chemical   heat   gravitational   kinetic

   Sam climbed up the steps of a slide, changing _____ energy to_____ energy, accelerated down the ramp, _____ energy to _____ energy and skidded to a halt at the end _____ energy to _____ energy.

5   1 kWh is the energy used in 1 hour by a device which has a power of 1000 W. How many kWh of energy do these devices use?

   a   A 250 W TV on for two hours.

   b   A 3 kW heater on for half an hour.

   c   A 1 kW drill on for fifteen minutes.

   d   A 60 W lamp for twelve hours.

6   Find the ratings plate on two electrical devices in your home. If 1 kWh of electrical energy costs 8 pence, calculate how long it takes to operate each device for 24 hours.

7   Jo gets hot climbing up a hill. She uses 27 MJ of chemical energy to gain 11 MJ of gravitational energy.

   a   Draw an energy diagram for Jo's energy transfers.

   b   How much heat energy does she gain?

   c   Show that her efficiency is about 40%.

8   A 100 W filament lamp transfers electricity to light energy with an efficiency of 5%. When the lamp is switched on for 1 minute

   a   How much electrical energy goes into the lamp?

   b   How much light energy comes out?

   c   What happens to the missing energy?

   d   Draw an energy transfer diagram for the lamp.

9   the sentence with the words **conduction**, **convection** or **radiation**.

   When coal is burnt in a grate, most of the heat energy enters the room by _____ .
   Some is carried up the chimney by _____.The rest goes through the grate to the floor by _____.

10 Explain, in detail, how energy is transferred from one place to another by

   a conduction   b convection

   c radiation   d evaporation.

11 Describe **six** different ways of reducing heat loss from a house. Explain how each of them works.

12 Design a box for keeping food cold on long bike journeys. Explain how it keeps the food cold.

13 Explain how the temperature inside an unheated greenhouse can be higher than outside.

14 Explain how electricity could be generated when fossil fuels have completely run out. Why would we need to use more than one method?

INTRODUCING
Keeping healthy

Shakeela keeps healthy by playing sports.

Try these first

1 Which of these do you need plenty of in a healthy diet?

   a proteins   b minerals

   c fats   d carbohydrates

   e nitrates

2 What are the differences between:

   a viruses and bacteria

   b antiseptics and disinfectants?

3 Why is it important to keep your skin clean?

In this unit you will learn:

- how your skin protects your body against entry of microbes
- how blood clotting seals wounds to protect you from infection
- how white blood cells destroy invading microbes
- how antibodies provide us with long-term immunity
- how kidneys filter the blood and maintain the body's correct water level
- how transplants or dialysis can help patients with kidney failure
- how enzymes control chemical reactions inside your body.

1 Taking care of your health

Public health care KH1

Everybody wants to be as healthy as they can – to avoid illness. Each of us can do something about our own health, but public health care involves the whole community.

Health care has changed dramatically over the past 125 years, not just because of advances in medical knowledge, but also because of improvements in general hygiene. These statistics show how common causes of death in the UK have changed over the years.

Common causes of death in the United Kingdom	
1876	**2000**
1 tuberculosis	**1** heart disease
2 diarrhoea and dysentery	**2** cancer
3 scarlet fever	**3** stroke

The three illnesses in the left-hand column are all caused by micro-organisms, or **microbes**, which get into the body and cause infection. Microbes include bacteria, viruses and some kinds of fungi. The pairs of pictures below show some of the changes that have helped to reduce the spread of **infectious illnesses** such as these.

When food is kept cold – in a fridge, for example – microbes that may be living in it reproduce much more slowly.

These days, cleaned and treated water is supplied directly to our homes.

Think about how each of these changes make it more difficult for microbes to survive and get into people's bodies.

Improvements in public health and hygiene have reduced the dangers of exposure to microbes, but cannot prevent it altogether. On the following pages, you will find out something about the ways in which our bodies resist entry of microbes, and about how the body protects itself against the harmful effects of any that do manage to get inside.

Different types of illness

Heart disease, cancer and strokes are not illnesses that are caused by bacteria, viruses or other microbes. They are examples of **non-infectious illnesses**. Other examples include nutritional problems, such as scurvy or pellagra, and allergies such as hayfever.

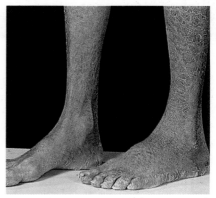

Pellagra causes painful cracks in the skin.

Pellagra – a medical detective story

Pellagra is a very painful illness that dries and cracks the skin. At the beginning of the 20th century, there were many cases of pellagra in the southern USA. The government sent Dr Joseph Goldberger to investigate.

The first stage of the investigation was to find exactly where the disease occurred. It was most common in orphanages and mental hospitals – places where large numbers of people were crowded together. Dr Goldberger had already investigated two other diseases that showed the same pattern – typhus and yellow fever. He had shown that both were infectious illnesses, spread by microbes.

The occurrence of pellagra showed one big difference from these other illnesses. Typhus and yellow fever affected both patients and staff in crowded institutions, but pellagra affected only the orphans or patients. Was this important? Before you read on, think what might cause this difference. What experiments could Dr Goldberger do to find out?

Dr Goldberger thought that diet might have an effect – at that time, staff had a more varied diet than the people they looked after. He arranged for many of the pellagra sufferers to be given fresh milk. Many recovered quickly. Was there something in milk that cured pellagra?

The next step was a larger, more controlled experiment. Dr Goldberger used prisoners from jails (they were encouraged to volunteer by being offered reductions in their sentences). The diagram shows how the experiment was done.

Even after this experiment, many doctors still believed that pellagra was infectious. So, for nearly a year, Dr Goldberger and his group lived and worked with pellagra sufferers. None of them caught pellagra.

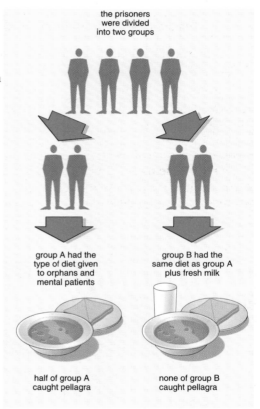

the prisoners were divided into two groups

group A had the type of diet given to orphans and mental patients

group B had the same diet as group A plus fresh milk

half of group A caught pellagra

none of group B caught pellagra

Dr Goldberger carried out a controlled experiment to see if milk in the diet helped to prevent pellagra.

Many years after, it was shown that pellagra is due to a shortage of nicotinic acid (also called niacin), which is one of the B group of vitamins. Milk, meat and flour all contain nicotinic acid. Before Dr Goldberger's work, people living in institutions were not given much meat or milk.

? Things to do

1 What made Dr Goldberger think that pellagra was a different kind of disease to typhus?
2 Do you think it is right to use people in experiments that may make them ill?

Why are some microbes harmful?

Many complex reactions go on inside the body. If any of these reactions go wrong, you become ill. Microbes can cause illness when they enter and grow inside your body. Once inside the body, microbes multiply rapidly. They can destroy tissue and produce substances that interfere with the processes inside the body. This makes us feel very ill.

Like all living things, microbes such as bacteria need:

- warmth
- moisture
- food.

Your body provides all of these for the microbes to grow.

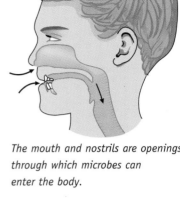

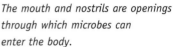

The mouth and nostrils are openings through which microbes can enter the body.

Skin – the first line of defence (SS) KH3

The outer layer of dead skin cells provides the body with its first line of defence against the entry of microbes. If the skin remains intact, it gives very good protection against bacteria.

However, there are various openings in the skin – parts of our body that are not protected by dead skin cells.
For example, we need openings in the skin to breathe!

This diagram shows places on the body where breaks or openings in the skin can allow entry of microbes.

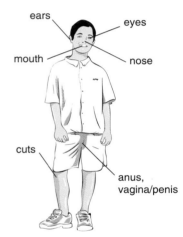

Microbes can invade through openings such as eyes and ears, and also through accidental breaks in the skin that happen when you cut yourself.

Mucous membranes

The lining of the nose, throat and lungs is called a **mucous membrane**.

- Mucous membranes make a sticky liquid called **mucus**. This forms a layer over the membrane. Microbes get stuck to it when you breathe them in.
- The membranes are covered with small hairs called **cilia**. These hairs waft the sticky mucus up the throat, so that it does not build up and block the lungs.

Tobacco smoke stops the cilia from working. This means there is more mucus in the lungs and more risk of infection, as the cilia are unable to remove the mucus and microbes.

What happens when you cut yourself? KH4, KH5, KH6

Shakeela injured her knee while running at school. It started to bleed.

After a short time, she noticed that the cut had stopped bleeding. Blood provides a second line of defence against entry of microbes, because it contains substances that **clot** (make a thick plug) and form a scab to cover wounds. Blood clots for two reasons:

- to stop more blood being lost
- to prevent microbes from entering the wound.

Blood circulates round the body. It carries food, oxygen and hormones to the tissues, and brings away carbon dioxide and other waste products.

Red blood cells contain **haemoglobin**, which combines with oxygen from the lungs and carries it round the body. **Platelets** are involved in blood clotting. **Plasma** is the liquid part of the blood.

White blood cells are involved in fighting any microbes that get into the body.

As she fell, Shakeela cut the skin on her knee, which could let microbes into her body.

How blood clots

When Shakeela cut her skin, the rough tissue caused platelets in her blood to burst open. The platelets released a chemical into her blood.

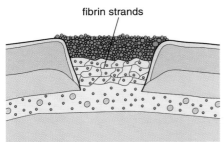

This chemical changes a soluble substance called fibrinogen in the blood into strands of solid fibrin. The strands tangle together and plug

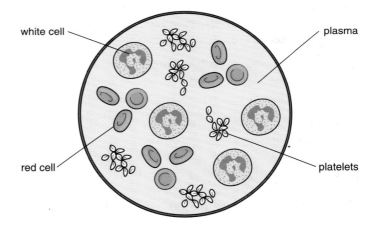

Blood is made up of lots of different things, all carried along in the liquid plasma.

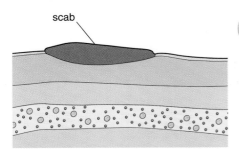

The plug is a dark colour because red blood cells get trapped in it. The plug gradually dries out to form a scab. The scab protects the new skin growing over the wound.

? Things to do

1   Write down all the things that make Shakeela's body a good place for microbes to grow.

2   Describe three ways that microbes could get into Shakeela's body.

3   Explain why people who smoke are more likely to get lung infections.

What do white blood cells do?

When Shakeela injured her knee, it is possible that some microbes entered the open wound. Her blood contains white blood cells. It is their job to fight infection and prevent her from becoming ill.

F

The blood contains two different kinds of white cells. They look the same, but work in different ways.

- Cells called **lymphocytes** use chemical warfare. They produce chemicals called **antibodies** that kill or label the microbes for destruction.

- Cells called **phagocytes** eat the microbes and digest them.

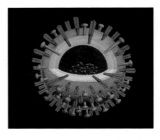

This 'flu' virus has particular chemicals on its outer surface, which lymphocytes recognise.

Recognising invaders (SS) KH7

Lymphocytes need to know the difference between the body's own cells and those of invading microbes. It would not be a good idea to destroy the body's own tissue!

Just as we recognise people by their surface features such as their face, lymphocytes recognise microbes by their surface features. The chemical structures on the surfaces of invading microbes are called **antigens**.

Shakeela's lymphocytes produced chemicals called antibodies. The antibodies attached themselves to the antigens on the microbes that invaded her injured knee. This labelled the microbes so that the phagocytes could find them and gobble them up.

Sometimes antibodies destroy invading cells directly. In other cases, they cause the invading cells to stick together in clusters that can be found easily by the phagocytes and gobbled up.

Allergies happen when the immune defence system over-reacts to contact with something that is normally not dangerous, causing symptoms of illness. For example, many people get hayfever – pollen in the air gives them sore eyes and a runny nose.

The human immuno virus (HIV) can attack the immune defence system. Some people can carry the virus for long periods without suffering any effects. If it does become active, it causes AIDS – a disease in which the person is less able to defend themselves against other infections.

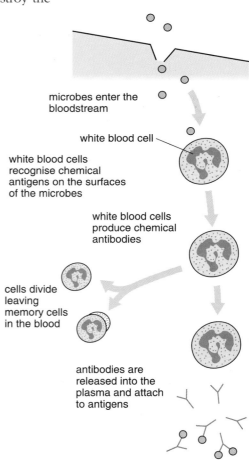

microbes enter the bloodstream

white blood cell

white blood cells recognise chemical antigens on the surfaces of the microbes

white blood cells produce chemical antibodies

cells divide leaving memory cells in the blood

antibodies are released into the plasma and attach to antigens

This way of fighting invading microbes is called the immune defence system.

Building up immunity

Shakeela went to the doctor for a check-up several days later. He examined the wound and found no trace of infection. The doctor explained that previous infections have taught her white blood cells to recognise any microbes that got into the wound.

Lymphocytes may take several days to make the antibodies to fight a new disease. This is more than enough time for the microbes to multiply and make us ill.

Once you have been infected with a particular type of microbe, antibodies against that microbe remain in your blood. These will be ready for immediate action if you are infected again. Some white cells that have learned to make these particular antibodies (called **memory cells**) remain in the blood. Any microbes that got into Shakeela's cut must have been types that she had met before. The microbes did not have a chance to multiply before they were destroyed. Shakeela was **immune** to the infection.

This is why, when you have a disease in childhood, like chicken pox, you do not catch the disease again as you get older – you are immune to that disease.

Immunisation (SS) KH8

Sometimes, when a disease is very dangerous, it is not worth the risk of catching the disease in order to produce your own antibodies. The disease might kill you first!

When you are **immunised** (or **vaccinated**) against an illness, you are injected with a very weak form of the microbe that causes the illness, or with a solution containing bits of the dead microbe. Your lymphocyte cells learn to recognise the antigens on the microbe. They make antibodies and these remain in your blood, ready for any real infection.

Active immunity

vaccine containing a weakened form of the microbe is injected

white blood cells produce chemical antibodies

some memory cells remain in your body

Passive immunity

serum containing antibodies is injected into the body

antibodies are ready to attack antigens immediately...

... but there is no long-term immunity because there are no memory cells

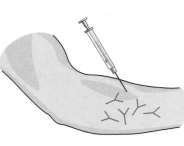

You have active immunity when your own body produces antibodies against a microbe, and these remain in your blood. You can be given temporary passive immunity with an injection of antibodies.

Things to do

1. Explain how an infection can spread round the body quickly once microbes have entered the bloodstream.

2. Explain the difference between antigens and antibodies

3. List the types of particles found in blood and explain what each type does.

4 Keeping your blood clean

What are your kidneys for?

Your blood transports food, oxygen and other chemicals around your body. It is important to remove waste products from blood, and also to keep a balance of the amount of water in your body. This is what your kidneys do.

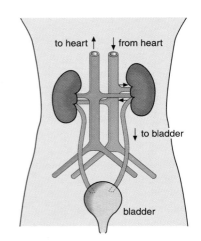

F
- It is the job of the kidneys to control the water content of the body.
- The kidneys also clean the blood by filtering urea from it.

Keeping a water balance (SS) KH10

It is important that the water content of the body remains almost constant. This means that any water taken in must be balanced by water leaving the body.

Your body absorbs water through:

- drinking
- water in the food you eat
- water produced by aerobic respiration

glucose + oxygen → carbon dioxide + **water**

Your body loses water through:

- sweat • urine • evaporation from the lungs.

The blood is filtered by the kidneys to produce urine. The amount of water in your body is kept in balance by controlling the amount of urine that is made.

'Water in' and 'water out' must always balance.

How is blood filtered?

The kidney is made up of thousands of tiny tubes, called **kidney tubules**. Blood enters the kidneys through a blood vessel, which divides into tiny capillaries going to each tubule.

The blood is under high pressure in the capillaries. The walls of the capillaries and tubules let small molecules through, so that they are filtered out of the blood. These small molecules are:

- water • glucose • salt
- urea (a waste product).

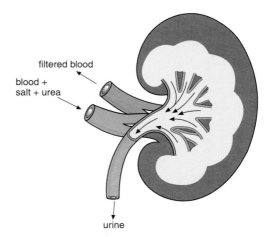

You have two kidneys, each with a good supply of blood.

Selective re-absorption

It is necessary to get rid of urea from the blood, as it is a potentially harmful waste product. But it is not a good idea to lose glucose, which is a food. As the filtered liquid, or filtrate, passes through the later stages of the kidney tubule, some of the small molecules move back into the blood in the capillaries. This is called **selective re-absorption**.

Molecules that are re-absorbed into the blood are:

- all of the glucose
- most of the water
- some of the salt
- none of the urea.

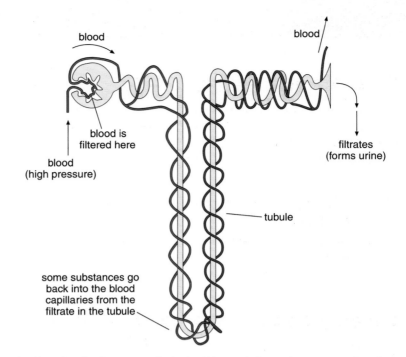

The filtered molecules are caught in the kidney tubules, to be transported to the bladder and excreted as urine.

When you are thirsty, the kidneys re-absorb more water back into the blood, and make very little urine.

When you have had a lot to drink, less water is re-absorbed and more urine is made.

The liquid that is left in the tubule will end up going to the bladder as urine, containing some water, all of the urea, and some salt.

Things to do

1   Describe the ways in which the body gains water and how it loses water.
2   Suggest why large molecules, like fibrinogen, are not filtered from the blood.
3   Suggest why it is not a good idea for all of the glucose to be filtered out of the blood.
4   Suggest a mechanism that would explain how the blood could re-absorb most of the water from the kidney tubule.
5   How would Shakeela's kidneys react if she drank too much water after her games lesson?
6   What do you think will happen to the concentration of Shakeela's urine if she goes a long time without drinking?

Dialysis – the artificial kidney (SS) KH11

On rare occasions, things can go wrong with the kidneys. They may become damaged by disease, or be injured during an accident. When this happens the kidneys can no longer carry out their job.

The main problem with kidney failure is that the waste substance urea builds up in the bloodstream. This substance is toxic and must be removed. In the past, if someone's kidneys stopped working, they would quickly become ill and die within a few days.

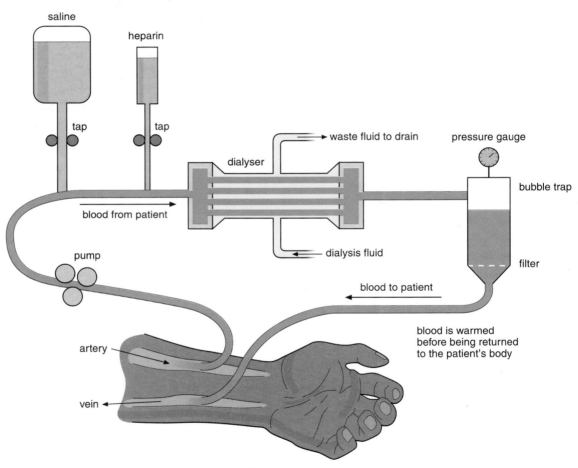

A kidney dialysis machine does the job of the failed kidneys – it 'cleans' the patient's blood to remove waste substances.

F During dialysis, salt solution (saline) is added to correct the salt balance in the blood. This job is normally carried out by the healthy kidneys.

A chemical called heparin is also added. This helps to stop the blood from clotting in the machine.

The bubble trap removes any small air bubbles from the blood before it is returned to the patient's body. The filter removes any blood clots that form. Clots or bubbles would be dangerous if they got back into the body.

An artificial kidney machine, or **dialysis machine**, takes some of the person's blood through a filter and then returns the cleaned blood to the body.

During dialysis, the blood flows through tubes made of artificial membranes. The small urea molecules are forced through pores in the membrane into the dialysis fluid.

Each session of treatment takes up to four hours and has to be repeated two or three times every week.

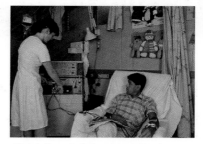

Abdul Khan is being kept alive by dialysis while he waits for a kidney transplant.

Kidney transplants

For people who are suffering from very severe kidney failure, an alternative treatment is to transplant a new kidney into the body.

Shakeela's parents always carry Donor Cards. This allows doctors to use their body organs for someone else, in the event of their death. This is how most patients with kidney failure get a new kidney.

Transplants are not always successful. The patient's immune system may recognise the new kidney as 'foreign' tissue and make antibodies to destroy it. This is called **rejection**.

One way to prevent rejection is to use drugs. Some drugs stop the immune system from working and producing antibodies. However, this means that the body also fails to produce antibodies to any disease-causing microbes that come along, so the patient may get a serious infection.

Another way to reduce the danger of rejection is to use a kidney from a close relative. There is less chance that the body will recognise this as being different from itself. This means that it will not produce antibodies to destroy it.

However, it usually means the relative has to donate a healthy kidney while still alive. This is not usually a problem as people can survive with only one working kidney.

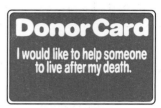

People carry Donor Cards in order to offer someone else the chance of a healthy life after their own death.

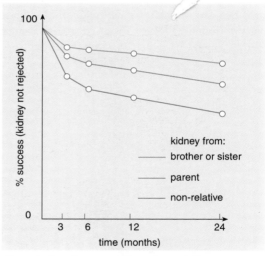

Transplants using organs from close relatives are more successful than those using an unrelated donor.

?

Things to do

1   State two different ways in which a person with kidney failure can be treated.

2   During dialysis, several things are done to the patient's blood. Explain the purpose of each of the following:

   a adding salt   b adding heparin   c using a bubble trap   d filtering the returning blood
   e warming the returning blood.

3   Explain why the body's immune system may react to a donated kidney.

4   Explain why transplants from close relatives are likely to be more successful.

What are enzymes? (SS) KH13

Many different chemical changes are going on inside your body. If any of these go wrong, or if they get out-of-step, this can make you ill. Chemical reactions inside plants and animals are all controlled by substances called **enzymes**.

Enzymes are sometimes called biological catalysts. They speed up chemical reactions, but are not used up during the reactions.

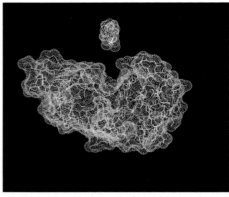

Computer graphics image of the enzyme ribonuclease showing a molecule approaching the active site.

Enzymes belong to the group of substances called **proteins**. They all have very large and complex molecules.

The part of the enzyme that controls the reaction is called the **active site**. The shape of this part of the molecule is very important. If the shape changes, the enzyme will not work.

Enzymes are **specific**. This means that each enzyme controls just one reaction. The substance whose reaction is controlled by the enzyme is called the **substrate** for the enzyme.

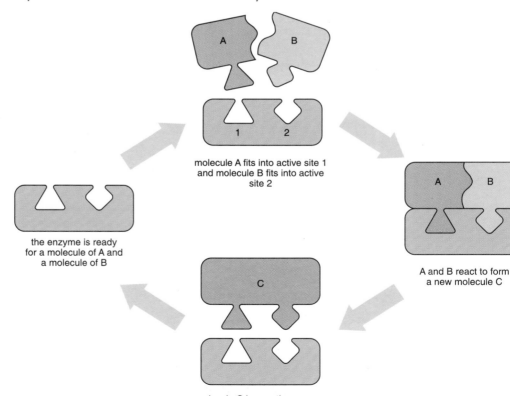

the enzyme is ready for a molecule of A and a molecule of B

molecule A fits into active site 1 and molecule B fits into active site 2

A and B react to form a new molecule C

molecule C leaves the enzyme

Enzymes speed up biological reactions by holding substrate molecules in position so that they can react.

The 'lock and key' model of how enzymes work

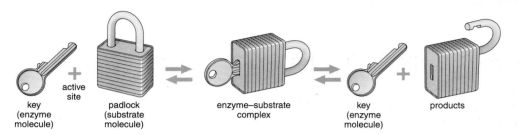

An enzyme helps a change to happen, a bit like a key changing a padlock from locked to unlocked.
At the end, the key itself is unchanged.

Enzymes	Lock and Key
One enzyme will only do one job.	A key will only open the correct lock.
Some chemical reactions won't work without an enzyme.	Some doors that are locked won't open without a key.
The shape of the active site of an enzyme is most important. The wrong shape will not work.	The shape of the 'teeth' of a key is most important. The wrong shape will not open the lock.

Enzymes are sensitive!

Enzymes are sensitive to any changes that might alter the shape of the enzyme molecule.

The shape of a protein molecule is changed by changes in pH (acidity) of the solution it is in. Many enzymes will work only within a very narrow range of pH. This is one reason why 'acid rain' has bad effects on plants. Some enzymes are designed to work under extremely acidic conditions. For example, digestive enzymes in your stomach have to work in a solution containing hydrochloric acid!

Temperature also has an effect on enzyme activity. Putting food in the fridge slows enzyme reactions in the food so that it keeps fresh for longer. When the food warms up again, the enzyme reactions speed up too.

Overheating can do permanent damage to enzymes and permanently change their shape. The enzyme is said to be **denatured**, and will not work again, even when it cools down.

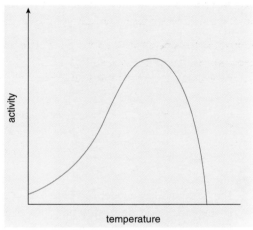

As the temperature rises, so does enzyme activity – until the enzyme becomes denatured. Then its activity falls suddenly to zero.

Things to do

1 Explain what is meant by a 'biological catalyst'.
2 Describe how the action of an enzyme is like a 'lock and key'.
3 Explain what happens to an enzyme as the temperature of the reaction increases.
4 Shakeela washes some clothes. She uses a biological washing powder. Explain why she should not set the washing machine to carry out a 'hot wash'.

7 Helpful drugs and not-so-helpful drugs

How do drugs affect your body?

Drugs can affect you in many different ways. One common way is by interfering with enzymes.

Some drug molecules work by blocking part of the active site of an enzyme. If the drug is carefully designed to block an enzyme in an invading bacterium, it can kill the bacterium or stop it growing.

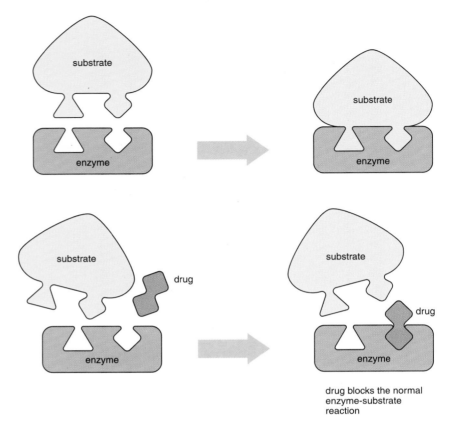

drug blocks the normal enzyme-substrate reaction

Some drugs work by blocking the normal activity of enzymes. The drug stops the substrate from getting into the active site.

F

The 'lock and key' model can help explain how enzyme blockers work. If someone sticks an obstruction into a lock, the key will no longer fit in, and the lock cannot be made to turn.

Drugs against everything?

Drugs can be made to work against bacteria, because bacteria rely on enzymes inside them to carry out life processes. The drug can be designed to block these enzymes, but not affect human cells.

Drugs can also be used to treat some non-infectious illnesses, such as metabolic disorders. The drug can be made to block enzymes affecting reactions that are out of balance in the body, to bring the reactions back into balance.

A new drug must be pure and safe to use, with very few side effects on the patient. Developing new drugs is very expensive and can take up to 20 years. This process may cost up to £100 million.

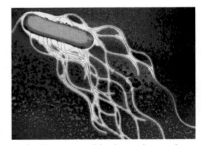

Infections caused by bacteria can be treated with drugs called antibiotics.

People can be vaccinated to help prevent them catching flu, but there are no drugs to treat people who have already caught the illness.

Fighting off flu

Flu (influenza) makes many people ill and kills large numbers every winter. It is caused by a virus.

Viruses rely on getting inside our cells and 'hijacking' our own enzymes to work for them. Antibiotics do not work against viruses.

A vaccine can now be used to immunise people against flu. It is given particularly to older people or those at special risk. Every year medical experts have to decide what type of vaccine to make as new types of flu viruses appear.

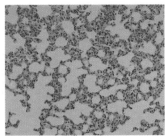

Healthy cilia remove mucus, dust and harmful microbes from the lungs

Drug abuse is dangerous

Some people take drugs for recreational reasons, rather than medical ones. Drugs and solvents affect the way the body works and they very often affect the brain too. This can affect behaviour.

For example, alcohol slows down people's reaction time, makes them more extrovert and more likely to behave aggressively. People who are drunk often behave in a way that they would not do if they were sober. Excessive long-term use of alcohol damages the liver and can result in death.

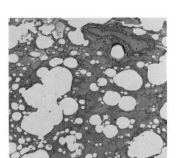

Healthy lung tissue, containing millions of tiny air sacs.

F All drugs alter the way your body works. This can be very dangerous, even with medical drugs. Some drugs not only affect your behaviour, but also damage the organs in your body.

Problems with addiction

Many drugs can cause addiction. As the dose of the drug wears off, unpleasant or painful symptoms are felt. In order to try to avoid this, the sufferer tries to obtain more of the drug. Because this is expensive, and most drugs can't be bought legally, this craving can easily lead to crime.

The effects of smoking

Cigarette smoke paralyses the cilia on the membranes lining the airways to the lungs. Mucus, microbes and particles of dirt build up in the lungs, which can then become infected.

Smoking can also damage the structure of the lungs. It breaks down the air sacs, resulting in a smaller surface area to absorb oxygen.

Damaged lung tissue, in which the walls between air sacs have been broken down, leaving a much smaller surface area.

Things to do

1 Explain why doctors sometimes do not prescribe any medicine for a sore throat.
2 Explain what effect alcohol can have on the body,
   a if taken in small amounts   b if consumed in large quantities over a period of time.
3 Explain why smoking often results in a shortness of breath.
4 Explain why many smokers suffer from bronchitis (an infection of the airways to the lungs).

1 Many illnesses are caused when pathogens enter through body openings. For each of the following openings, describe the defence method which protects against entry of pathogens:

a the eyes

b the nose

c the mouth

2 Describe how each of the following help to defend the body against microbes which enter through cuts in the skin:

a platelets

b plasma

c red blood cells

d white blood cells

3 Which one of the following statements about enzymes is NOT correct?

Enzymes -

a are sensitive to pH

b are destroyed by heat

c are used in the chemical industry

d do not work if the temperature is less than 30°C

4 A solution of the enzyme amylase was mixed with starch solution. Equal-sized samples of the mixture were kept at different temperatures and tested every minute with iodine. The table shows the time taken for all the starch to be digested in each sample.

Sample No	Temp/ °C	Time taken/min
1	0	More than 20
2	20	18
3	40	2
4	60	20
5	80	More than 20
6	98	More than 20

a Amylase acts as a catalyst in this reaction. Explain what is meant by a **catalyst**.

b What result would you expect to see when starch solution is tested with iodine?

c What chemical is starch changed into during digestion?

d How could you test for this chemical? Describe both how you would do the test, and what results you would expect

e Explain why the starch was not digested

i) in tube 1

ii) in tubes 5 and 6

f From the data given, what is the best temperature for the digestion of starch using amylase?

g Explain why it is a good idea to chew bread thoroughly before swallowing it.

5 In order to grow, bacteria need to make a chemical called folic acid. One of the chemicals used by bacteria to make folic acid is called PABA. An enzyme helps to convert this to folic acid. The diagram on the left shows the molecular structure of the PABA ion. The right-hand diagram shows sulphanilamide, used as a germicide.

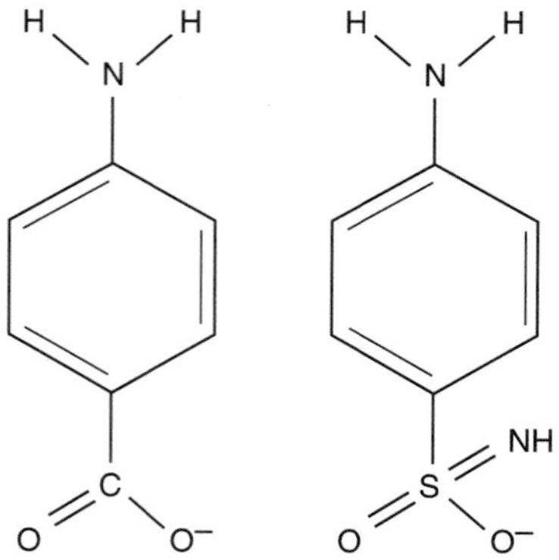

a State four similarities between the structures

b State one difference between them

c Explain as fully as you can, how sulphanilamide can act as a germicide.

INTRODUCING
Transporting chemicals

Try these first

Which of the following is the symbol for the element nitrogen?   N   Ni

Which of the following is the symbol for the element copper?   C   Co   Cu

Which of the following is the symbol for the element iron?   Fe   I   Ir

Most of the elements are metals. True or false?

Most of the elements are solids. True or false?

For each of the substances A, B, C and D, decide whether the substance is definitely an element, definitely *not* an element or *could be* an element.

A is a solid at room temperature.

B burns in air to form a single oxide.

C boils at 59 °C.

D decomposes on heating to form a black solid and a colourless gas.

What particles make up an element?

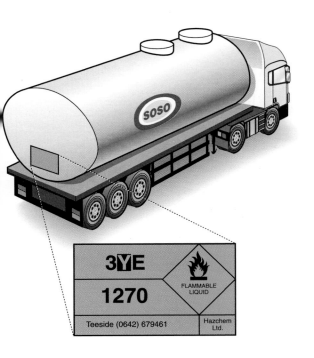

In this unit you will learn:

- that chemicals often have to be transported from where they are made to where they will be used
- that warning signs give information about hazards and how spills should be treated
- that symbols and formulas used for chemicals are the same in all languages
- that chemical equations show what happens in chemical reactions as new substances are formed
- that all substances are made up of elements
- that the elements are arranged in the Periodic Table which shows patterns in their properties
- that the Periodic Table was developed by the work of many scientists and allows you to make predictions about chemical reactions.

1 Chemicals on the move

Have you seen tanker lorries on the roads? How can you tell what they are carrying? Are there any dangers linked to the substances inside, or are they quite safe?

Tankers should always have hazard signs giving details about their load, in case there is an accident or spillage.

Hazardous cargoes (SS) TC1, TC2

It is cheaper to make petrol in a few large oil refineries, rather than in many small ones, so petrol often has to be carried quite long distances by road to local filling stations.

Petrol tankers and most other chemical tankers carry orange hazard signs, which tell about the chemical being carried.

3YE	
1270 Petrol	FLAMMABLE LIQUID
(0642) 679461	Hazchem Ltd.

If a tanker is carrying a hazardous substance such as petrol, it should carry an orange sign such as this.

Non-hazardous cargoes

Milk from farms is collected in tankers and taken to dairies. Lorries carrying non-hazardous cargoes like milk have white signs to show that the contents are safe if there should be an accident or a leak.

NON	
HAZARDOUS	
Dairy products	

Non-hazardous cargo still needs to be labelled, in case of an accident.

Labelling bottles and packages

Bottles of chemicals in your school laboratory have hazard warning signs on them. The same warning signs are on many household chemicals.

This bottle contains a chemical called hexane, which is a hydrocarbon liquid (like petrol). The warning sign makes it clear to everybody that hexane is flammable.

?

Things to do

1   These are some of the warnings you might see on bottles of chemicals.

toxic (poisonous)   corrosive   oxidising   harmful or **irritant   explosive   flammable**

Match each one to the symbol that would be used.

Find out the meanings of any words you don't know.

Lack of a label puts 600 children at risk

On Friday 23rd February 1996, a lorry caught fire on a road in Sydney, Australia. The lorry was carrying pigment (coloured powder) for making paints. People often don't think of 'everyday' chemicals as dangerous, so they are not always labelled.

The load of pigment on this lorry was lead chromate, which is used in yellow paints. The load was not labelled, but it should have been.

Emergency services are advised to cover spills of lead chromate with sand to stop the dust from spreading. Because this lorry was not labelled, the fire crew didn't know what was on board and they began spraying with water.

Some of the paper sacks of lead chromate burst, and clouds of fine yellow powder flew into the air. Just across the road, in West Epping School, 600 primary school children were having lessons. The children were evacuated quickly but 69 had to be taken to hospital.

Fortunately, none of the children, fire-fighters or other local people suffered any lasting harm.

TOXIC

Harmful by skin contact or inhaling dust. Causes irritation of the skin and may cause ulcers.

May cause symptoms of asthma.

Lead chromate is a carcinogen.

Here are some of the things the label on the lead chromate lorry should have said.

Things to do

2   Answer these questions about this story on this page.

   a Vehicles sometimes catch fire, because of faults with their engines, brakes or electrical wiring. What should you do if you see a vehicle on fire?

   b Lead chromate is a 'carcinogen'. What does this mean?

   c Why are pigments for paints supplied as a very fine powder?

   d Why is the fine powder especially dangerous?

   e Why didn't the fire-fighters know the best way to tackle the incident?

3   Look for hazard warnings on chemicals at home or in the supermarket. Make a table giving the name of the product, the active chemical it contains and the hazard sign shown.

4   Make a list of warning signs on chemicals in your school laboratory. For each one, list the chemicals that have this sign on them.

5   What is the advantage of including a hazard sign on the label rather than just a written warning?

2 Clear and simple warnings

The Hazchem code

Road tankers carrying chemicals show hazard warning signs on the side and back. These signs give information to the emergency services to help them deal safely with any accident or spillage.

The large number at the top of the sign is the internationally-recognised **Hazchem code**. It consists of a number followed by one or two letters.

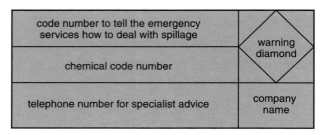

code number to tell the emergency services how to deal with spillage	warning diamond
chemical code number	
telephone number for specialist advice	company name

The Hazchem code is used all over the world to give clear details about the chemicals being carried, which everyone can understand.

- The *number* shows the type of treatment or equipment that should be used on spillages:

  1 = jets or water

  2 = fog (provides a fine spray of water droplets)

  3 = foam

  4 = dry agent.

- The *first letter* relates to the nature of the chemical. Some substances, indicated by the letters **P**, **R**, **S** or **T** can simply be mixed with large amounts of water (diluted) and washed away into surrounding soil or drains. Others indicated by **W**, **X**, **Y** or **Z** must not be allowed to enter drains and must be kept in place until they can be collected and disposed of.
- These letters also show whether emergency services need to wear full protective clothing or whether just breathing apparatus and gloves will be sufficient.
- If a second letter is used it will be **E**, and this shows that the emergency services should consider whether to evacuate (move away) people in nearby areas.

This table shows the meanings of the letters that make up the Hazchem code. (The letter V indicates where there is the possibility of a violent reaction – it is not shown on the lorry signs.)

Code	Reaction	Equipment	Action
P	V	full protective clothing	dilute (wash away)
R			
S	V	breathing apparatus	
T			
W	V	full protective clothing	contain spills
X			
Y	V	breathing apparatus	
Z			
E			consider evacuation

Codes for chemicals

Every chemical has a code number. This means that emergency workers can be sure about the identity of the chemical in the tanker without needing to understand chemical names.

The sign also shows a phone number that can be used to get extra advice, the name of the company responsible for the shipment, and a picture hazard symbol.

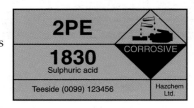

The code number for sulphuric acid is 1830.

Chemical hazard symbol

These hazard symbols appear in the 'warning diamond' of tanker hazard signs.

Cracking the Hazchem code

The example at the top of this page shows a hazard sign for concentrated sulphuric acid.

P shows that spills should be 'diluted'; that is, mixed with water to wash them away. The number **2** means that a fine spray of water, or 'fog', should be used on spills.

P shows that full protective clothing must be worn as the reaction of sulphuric acid with water can be violent.

Things to do

Write down the information given by each of these signs.

1.

2.

3.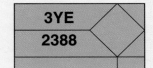

4.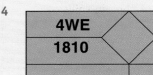

5.

3 Why transport chemicals?

Who makes chemicals?

The chemical industry takes **raw materials** – oil, gas, coal, salt or other minerals, air, water – and converts them by chemical reactions into many different chemicals. People buy and use some of these products (paints, cosmetics, detergents and so on), and others are used by other, different industries.

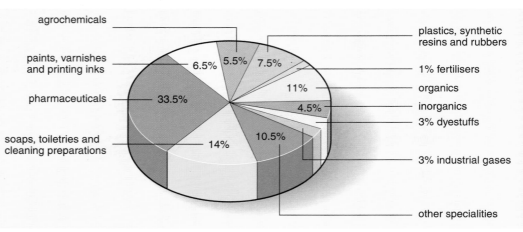

This chart shows the products from the UK chemical industry (by sale value, mid-1990s).

Ways of transporting chemicals

Chemicals have to be transported to where they are going to be used to make other materials. The method used to transport a particular chemical depends on the amount to be transported, how hazardous it is, whether it is solid, liquid or gas, and how urgent the delivery is.

Cost of transporting chemicals

Transport costs can be divided into **capital costs** and **running costs**. The capital costs are the costs of buying the equipment and getting it working. The running costs are the costs that have to be paid every day to keep the transport going.

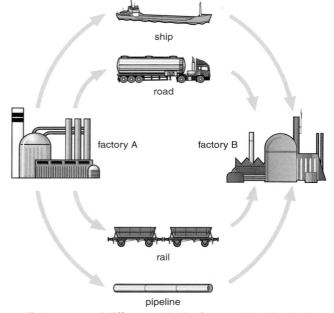

There are several different methods of transporting chemicals.

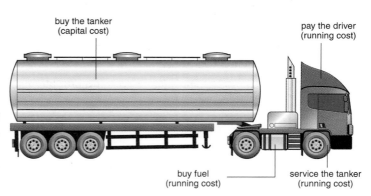

This diagram shows the costs of transporting chemicals by road tanker.

Chemicals from salt – the salt mines

In North Cheshire in England, there are vast underground salt deposits. Salt from these deposits is used in chemical works close to the salt mines.

In the factory, electricity is passed through salt solution and three substances are produced:

- sodium hydroxide solid
- chlorine gas
- hydrogen gas.

Huge diggers like this are used to transport salt up from underground deposits.

Transporting sodium hydroxide

Sodium hydroxide is a white solid, which readily absorbs water from the atmosphere. It is very soluble in water and its solution is very corrosive. It has many uses, including making:

- paper
- soap
- rayon (a fibre made from wood).

Factories that make these materials are often far away from the factories producing sodium hydroxide.

Transporting chlorine (SS) TC4

Chlorine is a poisonous gas, which changes easily to a liquid when you compress it. It is not flammable. It is produced in factories from salt and has to be delivered to different customers, who use it for:

- making polymers (plastics) such as PVC
- making solvents used for dry cleaning
- treating water to kill harmful bacteria.

Things to do

1. Which sector of the UK chemical industry produces the highest value of chemicals?
2. Suggest advantages and disadvantages of sending chemicals by each of the four methods shown in the diagram.
3. Chemicals are sometimes delivered through underground pipelines. What would be the capital costs and running costs for a pipeline?
4. Suggest how the underground salt deposits in North Cheshire could have been formed.
5. Why is it an advantage to build factories that use salt close to a salt mine?
6. Suggest reasons why factories making paper, soap or rayon may not be close to a factory producing sodium hydroxide.
7. Which method would you suggest to transport chlorine? Give reasons for your choice.

Chemical symbols

Just as the code on Hazchem labels is international, so there is a code used by chemists the world over to represent pure elements and compounds.

There are more than 100 elements, and each is represented by a single letter or two letters of the alphabet. This is called the **symbol** of the element. You can find the symbol for an element by looking at the **Periodic Table**.

A compound is represented by a **formula**. The formula is made up of the symbols of the elements in the compound, and numbers that show how many atoms of each element are present.

The formula for calcium chloride is $CaCl_2$. This means that calcium chloride is made up from the elements calcium and chlorine and that there are two atoms of chlorine for every one atom of calcium.

Sometimes you will see brackets in chemical formulas. For example, calcium hydroxide is represented by $Ca(OH)_2$. This is a shorthand way of writing CaO_2H_2 – the small number after the bracket multiplies everything in the bracket.

三氧化硫跟水化合生成硫酸，同时放出大量的热。

$$SO_3 + H_2O \longrightarrow H_2SO_4$$

硫酸虽然是三氧化硫跟水化合而制得的，但工业上不是直接用水或稀硫酸来吸收三氧化硫的。因为用水或稀硫酸来吸收容易形成发烟硫酸，不利于工业生产。

Here is part of a page from a Chinese chemistry book. How much of it can you read?

Žveplov trioksid nato reagira z vodo, pri tem pa nastane žveplova kislina.

žveplov trioksid + voda → žveplova kislina
$$SO_3 + H_2O \rightarrow H_2SO_4$$

Now look at this page from a Slovenian text book.

? Things to do

1   What do the following formulas of compounds tell you about the elements present?

  a sodium chloride, NaCl

  b aluminium chloride, $AlCl_3$

  c aluminium oxide, Al_2O_3

  d sodium sulphate, Na_2SO_4

2   What do the following formulas of compounds tell you about the elements present?

  a copper(II) nitrate, $Cu(NO_3)_2$

  b ammonium sulphate, $(NH_4)_2SO_4$

  c aluminium sulphate, $Al_2(SO_4)_3$

Rules about formulas

There are patterns in the formulas of compounds. These patterns will help you remember how many atoms of each type are needed.

The **combining power** of an element is the number of links formed by one atom of the element. In many simple compounds, each element has a fixed combining power. Groups also have a fixed combining power.

Compounds of two elements

Look at the formulas of the compounds in the table. Notice that each atom of sodium can only form a link with *one* other atom – it has a combining power of 1.

Chlorides	Bromides	Iodides	Oxides
NaCl	NaBr	NaI	Na_2O
KCl	KBr	KI	K_2O
$MgCl_2$	$MgBr_2$	MgI_2	MgO
$CaCl_2$	$CaBr_2$	CaI_2	CaO

Compounds of more than two elements

Of course these can be more complicated! However, certain groups of atoms which often occur together always have the same formula and the same combining power.

Hydroxides	Sulphates	Carbonates
NaOH	Na_2SO_4	Na_2CO_3
KOH	K_2SO_4	K_2CO_3
$Mg(OH)_2$	$MgSO_4$	$MgCO_3$
$Ca(OH)_2$	$CaSO_4$	$CaCO_3$

Things to do

3   In the compounds of two elements (in the first table above), what is the combining power of:

a potassium   b magnesium

c calcium   d chlorine

e bromine   f iodine

g oxygen?

4   In the compounds of more than two elements (in the second table above), what is the combining power of:

a hydroxide   b sulphate

c carbonate?

Equations for reactions

In chemical reactions, new substances are formed.

The diagram shows a **chemical change**. The starting chemicals, magnesium and oxygen, are called **reactants** – they change into a different chemical, magnesium oxide, which is called the **product**.

This can be summarised in a **word equation**.

magnesium + oxygen → magnesium oxide

Word equations tell you which substances are involved in a chemical reaction, but not how much of each!

The reaction can also be represented as a **symbol equation**.

$$2Mg + O_2 \rightarrow 2MgO$$

The equation tells you that 2 atoms of magnesium (Mg) react with 1 molecule of oxygen (O_2) to form 2 molecules of magnesium oxide (MgO).

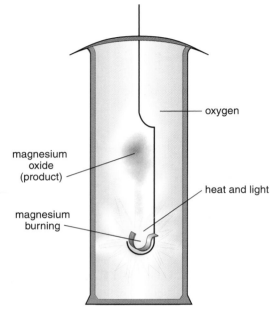

Solid magnesium metal burns in oxygen gas to form a white solid called magnesium oxide.

In a chemical reaction, atoms are rearranged to form new substances. No atoms are lost and no new atoms are created. In the symbol equation above, that is why '2' is placed in front of the 'Mg' and in front of the 'MgO'. The total number of atoms of each element on the left must always be equal to the total number on the right. The equation is **balanced**.

Notice that the large number placed in front of a formula multiplies the whole of the formula.

You will see lots of these symbol equations. They give more information than word equations. They are used by chemists throughout the world – they are the international language of chemistry.

? Things to do

1   Work out the total number of atoms of each type in:

   a Na_2SO_4 b $(NH_4)_2SO_4$

   c 3NaOH   d $2Cu(NO_3)_2$

Balancing equations

The following two equations are balanced.

$$2Fe + 3Cl_2 \rightarrow 2FeCl_3$$

$$Ca(OH)_2 + 2HCl \rightarrow CaCl_2 + 2H_2O$$

They are called balanced equations because they have the same number of atoms of each element on each side of the equation. Try it – for each equation, count the number of atoms of each element on each side and you will see that they are balanced.

This equation is not balanced.

$$CO + O_2 \rightarrow CO_2$$

Count the number of atoms of each element on each side. Then, by putting the appropriate numbers in front of the formulas, try to make the equation balance. Remember you cannot change a formula!

Understanding state symbols

Sometimes one or two letters are written in brackets after the formula of a substance. These show the state of the substance, that is whether it is a solid, liquid or gas, or if it is dissolved in water. For example:

NH_3 (g) means ammonia gas

and NH_3 (aq) means ammonia dissolved in water.

?

Things to do

2 Find out what each of these State symbols means:

A (g)   **B** (l)   **C** (s)   **D** (aq)

3 **A** C_2H_4O **B** $CaCO_3$ **C** $C_2H_4O_2$ **D** Cl_2

From the formulas **A** to **D**, choose the one that:

a contains the element calcium

b contains only one element

c represents the greatest number of atoms

d contains the elements carbon, oxygen and hydrogen in the ratio 2 : 1 : 4.

4 **A** $CH_4 + 2O_2 \rightarrow CO_2 + 2H_2O$ **B** $Mg + Cl_2 \rightarrow MgCl_2$

   C $Fe + H_2SO_4 \rightarrow FeSO_4 + H_2$ **D** $H_2 + Cl_2 \rightarrow HCl$

From the equations **A** to **D**, choose the one that:

a represents a reaction that produces hydrogen

b represents a reaction between a metallic element and a non-metallic element to form a compound

c represents the burning of a fuel to produce carbon dioxide and water

d is not a balanced equation.

6 Getting the elements in order

1789

It was the year of the French Revolution. A French nobleman called Antoine Lavoisier published a book in which he classified the elements.

He did this by grouping elements with similar properties together. He might have made further progress with this but the revolutionaries chopped off his head with the guillotine in 1794!

Antoine Lavoisier published his 'Table of Substances' in the 18th century.

1863

The story continued when John Newlands, a British chemist, arranged all the known elements in order of increasing mass of their atoms. He noticed that when they were arranged like this there was a pattern in their properties. At a meeting of the Chemical Society in London he announced that:

Newlands compared chemistry with music, which many scientists found so strange that they simply dismissed all of his ideas.

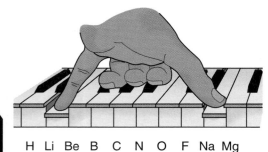

H Li Be B C N O F Na Mg

The pattern of properties, which repeated every eight elements, became known as Newlands' Octaves.

This pattern or generalisation only worked for the first 16 elements. This fact, plus the way Newlands linked the pattern to musical notes, led some of the other chemists at the meeting to ridicule his idea.

The repetition of similar properties at regular intervals is called **periodic variation**. Although other people did not accept Newlands' generalisation at the time, it was the beginning of the Periodic Table of the elements that scientists now accept and understand.

John Newlands, a 19th century British chemist with some interesting ideas.

1869

Dimitri Mendeleev, a Russian scientist, published another Periodic Table. The basic idea was the same as Newlands' arrangement. Mendeleev:

- arranged the elements in order of the masses of their atoms
- put elements with similar properties under each other in columns.

Earlier ideas had failed because not all of the elements had been discovered. Mendeleev realised this and where the pattern did not fit, he left spaces in his table. He predicted that other elements would be discovered to fill the spaces. Mendeleev was using his pattern to predict the properties of elements not yet known.

For example, Mendeleev realised that arsenic (As) fitted better under phosphorus (P) than under silicon (Si). He predicted that the undiscovered element to fill the space would form a white oxide with two atoms of oxygen for each one of the new element.

Dimitri Mendeleev was Professor of Chemistry at St Petersburg University in Russia, during the 19th century.

1884 (SS) TC10

Fifteen years later, the missing element was discovered. It is called germanium (Ge) and it does indeed form a white oxide, with formula GeO_2. Chemists began to believe that the Periodic Table was useful.

Mendeleev did not suggest an explanation for the periodic pattern. This happened much later when theories about the structures of atoms were developed.

	Group 1	Group 2	Group 3	Group 4	Group 5	Group 6	Group 7	Group 8
Period 1	H							
Period 2	Li	Be	B	C	N	O	F	
Period 3	Na	Mg	Al	Si	P	S	Cl	
Period 4	K	Ca	?	Ti	V	Cr	Mn	Fe Co Ni
	Cu	Zn	?	?	As	Se	Br	
Period 5	Rb	Sr	Y	Zr	Nb	Mo	?	Ru Rh Pd
	Ag	Cd	In	Sn	Te	I		

Mendeleev realised that where the repeating pattern of properties seemed broken, there was probably an element missing that had not yet been discovered.

? Things to do

1. Give a reason why scientists wanted to classify the elements.

2. A magazine that is published at regular intervals, such as once a month, is called a periodical. Why do you think the table of elements is called the Periodic Table?

3. Write a short newspaper article reporting on the Chemical Society meeting in London at which Newlands announced his 'Law of Octaves'.

4. Lavoisier, Newlands and Mendeleev all published their ideas. Why do you think scientists publish their results and the theories they have based on them?

5. Mendeleev's Periodic Table is a generalisation, or scientific law, but it is not a *theory*. Use ideas from this page to explain why this is so.

Listing elements

One way to arrange the elements is in order of the masses of their atoms, placing the lightest element first.

If you do this, you might notice that similar elements appear at fairly regular intervals. For example, lithium, sodium, and potassium are all soft metals that react with water to produce hydrogen gas and a basic solution.

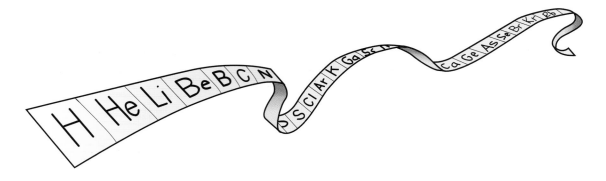

? Things to do

1 The vertical columns numbered 1–7 and 0 are called groups.

a In which group is the family of elements called alkali metals?

b In which group is the family of elements called halogens?

c In which group is the family of elements called noble gases?

2 What is the significance of the bold line drawn on the Periodic Table?

Group number

relative atomic mass

	1
name →	H ← symbol:
	Hydrogen
	1
	↑ atomic number

black solid
blue liquid
red gas
white synthetically prepared
most stable isotope

	1	2							
1	1 H Hydrogen 1								
2	7 Li Lithium 3	9 Be Beryllium 4							
3	23 Na Sodium 11	24 Mg Magnesium 12							
4	39 K Potassium 19	40 Ca Calcium 20	45 Sc Scandium 21	48 Ti Titanium 22	51 V Vanadium 23	52 Cr Chromium 24	55 Mn Manganese 25	56 Fe Iron 26	59 Co Coba 27
5	86 Rb Rubidium 37	88 Sr Strontium 38	89 Y Yttrium 39	91 Zr Zirconium 40	93 Nb Niobium 41	96 Mo Molybdenum 42	97 Tc Technicium 43	101 Ru Ruthenium 44	103 Rh Rhod 45
6	133 Cs Caesium 55	137 Ba Barium 56	139 La Lanthanum 57	179 Hf Hafnium 72	181 Ta Tantalum 73	184 W Tungsten 74	186 Re Rhenium 75	190 Os Osmium 76	192 Ir Iridiu 77
7	223 Fr Francium 87	226 Ra Radium 88	227 Ac Actinium 89	104	105	106	107	108	109

Period number

Lanthanide series	140 Ce Cerium 58	141 Pr Praseodymium 59	144 Nd Neodymium 60	145 Pm Promethium 61	150 Sm Samarium 62	152 Eu Europi 63
Actinide series	232 Th Thorium 90	231 Pa Protoactinium 91	238 U Uranium 92	237 Np Neptunium 93	242 Pu Plutonium 94	243 Am Americ 95

Tabulating elements

The classification can be improved – instead of having the elements in one long row, a new row is started every time you come to one of these similar elements.

This arrangement is more compact than a long list. If you look closely at it, you will see other examples of elements in the same vertical column having similar properties.

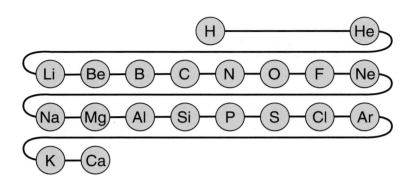

Remember that the table is continuous, but a new row is started at periodic intervals so that similar elements are under one another. The horizontal rows are called periods. The vertical columns that contain similar elements are called groups.

The Periodic Table

The Periodic Table is a more complete table to show relationships between all of the elements. The numbers under the symbols show the order of the elements in the table. The number for each element is called its **atomic number**.

								0
								4 **He** Helium 2
alkali metals			3	4	5	6	7	
alkaline earth metals			11 **B** Boron 5	12 **C** Carbon 6	14 **N** Nitrogen 7	16 **O** Oxygen 8	19 **F** Fluorine 9	20 **Ne** Neon 10
transition metals								
rare earth metals			27 **Al** Aluminium 13	28 **Si** Silicon 14	31 **P** Phosphorus 15	32 **S** Sulphur 16	35.5 **Cl** Chlorine 17	40 **Ar** Argon 18
halogens								
noble gases	63.5 **Cu** Copper 29	65 **Zn** Zinc 30	70 **Ga** Gallium 31	73 **Ge** Germanium 32	75 **As** Arsenic 33	79 **Se** Selenium 34	80 **Br** Bromine 35	84 **Kr** Krypton 36
other non metals	108 **Ag** Silver 47	112 **Cd** Cadmium 48	115 **In** Indium 49	119 **Sn** Tin 50	122 **Sb** Antimony 51	128 **Te** Tellurium 52	127 **I** Iodine 53	131 **Xe** Xenon 54
	197 **Au** Gold 79	201 **Hg** Mercury 80	204 **Tl** Thallium 81	207 **Pb** Lead 82	209 **Bi** Bismuth 83	210 **Po** Polonium 84	210 **At** Astatine 85	222 **Rn** Radon 86
	111	112	113	114	115	116	116	118

159 **Tb** Terbium 65	162 **Dy** Dysprosium 66	165 **Ho** Holmium 67	167 **Er** Erbium 68	169 **Tm** Thulium 69	173 **Yb** Ytterbium 70	175 **Lu** Lutetium 71
247 **Bk** Berkelium 97	249 **Cf** Californium 98	254 **Es** Einsteinium 99	253 **Fm** Fermium 100	256 **Md** Mendelevium 101	254 **No** Nobelium 102	257 **Lr** Lawrencium 103

?

Things to do

3   There are many different forms of the Periodic Table. Find other examples of Periodic Tables in books or on the Internet.

1   The formula for vitamin C is $C_6H_8O_6$. The formula is the same whether the vitamin C is made (synthesised) artificially or extracted from orange juice.

a   What information does the formula give about vitamin C?

b   Discuss whether there is any difference between natural and synthetic vitamin C.

2   These bottles of chemicals are in a store in a school in Germany.

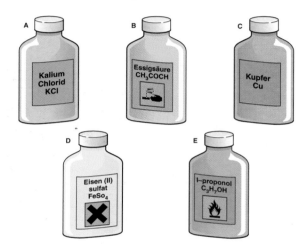

a   Which bottle contains an element?

b   Which bottle contains an irritant?

c   Which bottle contains a compound of potassium?

d   Which bottles contain compounds of carbon?

e   Why are chemical formulas, or codes, more useful than names when chemicals are transported from one country to another?

3   The formula for sodium nitrate is $NaNO_3$

a   What is the combining power of the nitrate group?

b   Write the correct formulas for:

i   calcium nitrate

ii   aluminium nitrate.

4   The hazard warning label shown below is carried on tankers delivering petrol.

a   If there is a fire:

i   what fire-fighting agent should be used?

ii   what protective clothing should be worn?

b   What should be done to the petrol if it leaks out of the tanker?

c   Petrol contains heptane, formula C_7H_{16}.

i   Which elements are present in heptane?

ii   How many atoms does one molecule of heptane contain?

iii   The equation for heptane burning is

$$C_7H_{16} + 11O_2 \rightarrow 7CO_2 + 8H_2O$$

Name the products of this reaction.

5   The pigment involved in the lorry fire on page 33 was lead chromate, formula $PbCrO_4$.

a   Write down the names of the elements in lead chromate.

b   What information does the formula give about the number of atoms of each element in lead chromate?

c   Lead chromate is made by mixing solutions of lead nitrate, $Pb(NO_3)_2$, and potassium chromate, K_2CrO_4.

i   Write a word equation for the reaction producing lead chromate.

ii   Write a balanced symbol equation for this reaction.

6   Look back at the combining powers of some elements on page 39.

a   Is there any pattern between the combining power and the position of the element in the Periodic Table?

b   Predict the formulas of:

i   boron chloride

ii   strontium oxide

iii   caesium chloride

iv   magnesium fluoride.

INTRODUCING
Construction materials

All kinds of materials are used for construction.

Try these first

Here are three metals in order of reactivity.

sodium (most reactive)

iron

silver   (least reactive)

1   Which metal reacts with water?

2   Which metal does not react with dilute acid?

3   What two things does iron need to rust?

4   Write down two ways in which you can stop iron from rusting.

5   Getting rid of acid is called:

condensation   neutralisation   corrosion

In this unit you will learn:

- that the properties of a material (for example, strength, or how easily it melts) depend on its structure (how its atoms are held together)
- that plastics are small molecules (monomers) joined to make long chain polymers
- that corrosion is caused by oxidation of metals
- that metals react with water and acids to make hydrogen
- that limestone (calcium carbonate) reacts with acids to make carbon dioxide
- that the rate of a reaction depends on concentration, surface area and temperature.

1 Built to last for ever?

Part of a law of King Hammurabi of Babylonia, about 2200 BC reads: *"If a builder builds a house that is not firmly constructed and it collapses and causes the death of its owner, that builder shall be put to death."*

Even without such penalties, builders want buildings to last. As new and stronger materials have been developed bigger, more complex buildings become possible.

Protecting buildings from wear and tear

Houses, schools, factories, shops and public buildings play an important part in our lives. They are expensive to build and are made to last as long as possible.

However tough materials are, they will eventually wear out. They can be made to last longer by careful design or by protection such as regular painting. In this unit, you will find out about some of the materials used in construction, and about how to take care of the finished buildings.

Buildings are designed and built to try to protect them from water damage.

Water damages building materials in three ways:

1 Water gets into cracks and if it freezes it expands, making the cracks wider.

2 Water contains micro-organisms such as fungi and algae, which cause rotting.

3 Rainwater can contain acids, which attack metals and some building stones.

? Things to do

1 Look around your school. What materials have been used in building it?

2 How are the materials on the outside of the buildings protected against the weather?

3 Look at a wooden fence. See if you can find cracks from frost damage, or any evidence of micro-organisms (algae are green, and fungi are often black and feel slimy).

Sometimes buildings need repairs. North West Water own the land around Hope Carr Barn. They plan to make a nature reserve and turn the old barn into an education centre.

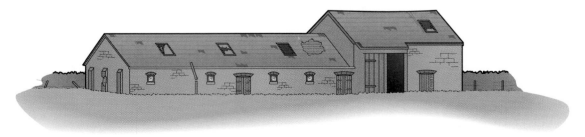

Hope Carr Barn, after 30 years of disuse.

This is a copy of the Surveyor's report for the barn.

Smith and Smith Chartered Surveyors

Main Street, Kenwall, KS20 9QT

Hope Carr Barn: Preliminary Survey Report

Survey date: 20th February

Weather: very wet

The barn is about 100 years old. It consists of a milking shed and a main barn.

Roof

The roof is of Welsh slate. Fascia boards are flush with the walls. Rainwater gutters and down spouts are of painted iron, but are heavily corroded. Many are missing.

General condition is poor. There is wet rot in the exposed roof timbers. 25% of the slates are damaged or missing because the iron nails holding them have corroded.

Walls

The outside walls are mainly of brick – solid constructions with no damp proof course. The mortar between bricks is damaged and flaky, allowing water to penetrate the bricks and cause frost damage. An older section of the gable wall is built of limestone blocks. This wall is sound, although there are signs of water damage due to missing gutters.

Joinery

All door and window frames are wooden and require replacing due to wet and dry rot.

Things to do

Read the surveyor's report, and answer these questions.

1   Why is it important to have a survey done on a building before you buy or renovate it?

2   Why is it important for the surveyor to record what the weather was like at the time of the inspection?

3   Draw a table like this one, to include all the building materials mentioned in the report.

Material	Use(s)	Useful properties	Unhelpful properties	Manufactured or naturally occurring
glass	windows	transparent, does not corrode, easy to cut to size	brittle, sharp edges	manufactured

4   Make a list of the jobs you would need to do on the roof, walls and woodwork if you were going to renovate the barn.

Decide whether you would use the same materials or whether you would replace them with modern alternatives.

2 Materials by design

Different materials behave in different ways. For any job, the right choice of material is important. If no natural material can be found, chemists or materials scientists try to design and manufacture one.

Plastics are made when lots of small molecules (**monomers**) join together to make larger molecules (**polymers**). This is called **polymerisation**. The monomers usually come from crude oil.

Thermoplastic polymers melt when they are heated and go solid when they cool. They have long, tangled molecules (like spaghetti). The molecules can slide over each other when the plastic is stretched or heated.

Thermosetting polymers do not melt when they get hot. They are hard and rigid, not stretchy. They have cross-links which stop the chains from sliding.

More about polymers (SS) CM1

Addition polymers are made when monomers simply add together (addition reactions are explained in the year 11 unit *Making use of oil*). Addition polymers are usually thermosoftening.

Some monomers can only be linked if a few atoms are removed to make bonds available. The atoms removed make small molecules like water. This is called **condensation** polymerisation. Most thermosetting plastics are condensation polymers.

If two different types of monomer molecules are linked, the polymer is called a co-polymer.

Nylon and terylene are examples of co-polymers. The properties of a polymer can be controlled by choosing the right monomers.

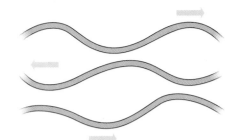

Molecules in thermoplastic polymers can slide over each other.

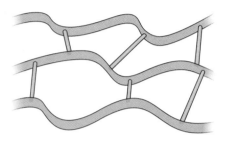

Cross-links stop thermosetting polymer chains from sliding.

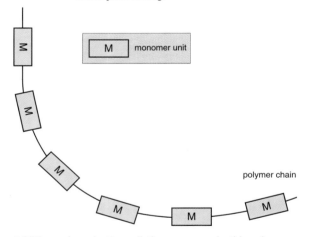

M monomer unit

polymer chain

Addition polymerisation: all the monomers in this polymer are the same.

monomers   A   B   A   B

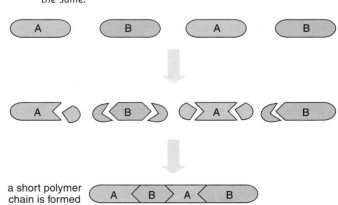

Condensation polymerisation: this polymer is made of two monomers. Water is also made.

a short polymer chain is formed

small molecules 'condense out'

Ceramics – improving on nature CM2

Ceramics are made by heating earthy materials. Bricks and pottery are ceramics made from clay. Clay contains aluminium, silicon and oxygen atoms bonded together in flat layers. Wet clay feels slippery.

Firing clay (heating it strongly in a kiln) drives out the water. The atoms in one layer make permanent cross-links with atoms in other layers.

It is very important to keep water out of brick because if it gets into even tiny cracks it might freeze in the winter. When the water freezes it expands causing the brick to crack and crumble.

Pottery is also made from clay, but it is fired at higher temperatures, which makes it more water-proof. Pottery surfaces that do not absorb water are very useful in bathrooms and kitchens.

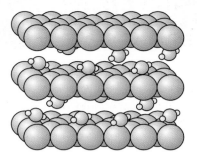

There are water molecules between the layers so that they easily slide over each other.

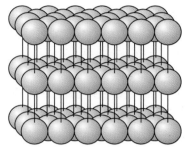

Cross-links make the brick hard and strong.

? Things to do

1 Make notes about the different types of polymers and how they are made.

2 Discuss which type of polymer would be best for making moulded objects like window frames.

3 Thin sheets of plastic are often used as damp-proofing to stop water rising through walls or floors What properties make plastic a good material for this use?

4 Monomers with small molecules are often gases or liquids, but polymers are solids. Use ideas about particles to explain this.

5 These boxes describe the **uses** and **properties** of some materials.

   These boxes use the **structures** of the materials (not in the same order).

Graphite is used to make pencils because it can rub off on paper to make marks.

It is made of long-chain molecules that can slip over each other.

Teflon is used to line ovens because it is hard and does not melt when it is hot.

It is layered. Layers can flake off easily.

Nylon is used to make fishing line. It is strong but stretchy and so does not snap easily.

It has cross-links between molecules. The molecules cannot move about, even at high temperatures.

Join each box on the left to the correct structure which explains the properties of the material.

3 Making use of metals

Most buildings have some parts made of metals (e.g iron nails, copper water pipes, steel radiators). You will find out how these metals are made in the unit *Mining and minerals*.

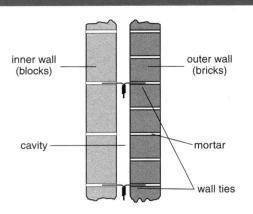

inner wall
(blocks)

outer wall
(bricks)

cavity

mortar

wall ties

Hidden metals – wall ties

The surveyor of Hope Carr Barn suggested building an outer brick wall to make a double wall with a cavity (space) between the two layers. Double walls have 'wall ties' to hold the two layers together.

Old buildings have wall ties made of iron. Newer wall ties are made of galvanised steel or stainless steel.

Old buildings have wall ties made of iron.

How does the weather affect iron?

 CM3

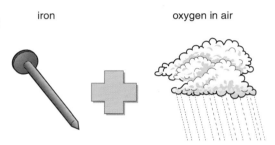

iron

oxygen in air

water

rust

Iron rusts when it is in contact with oxygen and water.

The guttering on the old barn was made of iron. It had rusted very badly.

When iron rusts it reacts with oxygen in the air. Rusting happens when the iron gets wet.

Other metals and corrosion

When other metals react with oxygen it is called **corrosion**. Some metals, such as silver, are very unreactive and so corrode very slowly.

When aluminium corrodes the aluminium oxide makes a waterproof and airproof coating. The aluminium underneath is protected, so it does not corrode. This makes aluminium useful for door and window frames.

Iron gutters and drainpipes become badly damaged by rust.

Protecting iron with other metals **CM4**

Iron can be protected from rusting by coating it with paint or grease. It can also be protected using other metals, for example zinc or chromium.

All these metals are 'transition metals'. Transition metals often have low chemical reactivity. They are useful because they resist corrosion.

Galvanised iron is coated with a layer of zinc.

Metals of different reactivity

You probably already know something about the reactivity series of metals.

Metals vary greatly in reactivity. Potassium reacts violently with cold water.

Silver is so unreactive that it is used in making coins and jewellery.

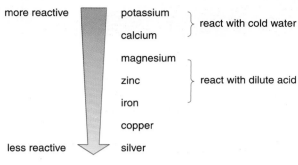

The reactivity series of metals.

Displacement reactions

More reactive metals can displace or 'kick out' less reactive metals from their chemical compounds.

For example, when an iron nail is dipped into copper sulphate solution, it turns orange. Some of the iron dissolves and takes the place of copper, which is 'kicked out' and forms a coating on the nail.

Iron + copper sulphate → copper + iron sulphate

$$Fe + CuSO_4 \rightarrow Cu + FeSO_4$$

Putting iron in contact with a less reactive metal makes the iron rust faster. If iron is in contact with a more reactive metal, for example zinc, then the more reactive metal corrodes and the iron is protected. Pieces of magnesium are sometimes fixed to ships' hulls to protect them from rust.

? Things to do

Sue tried some experiments investigating displacement. Look at the results of her experiments. Answer these questions .

1 What observations would you expect when zinc is added to copper sulphate solution?

2 Use the reactivity series to predict whether iron would react with zinc sulphate solution.

3 Would a coating of copper protect iron from rusting? Explain your answer.

4 Write word and symbol equations for the reactions in Sue's results table.

Metal + Solution	Observation	Conclusion
Iron + copper sulphate	Brown solid made copper	Iron more reactive than copper
Zinc + lead sulphate	Grey crystals seen lead	Zinc more reactive than lead
Zinc + copper sulphate		

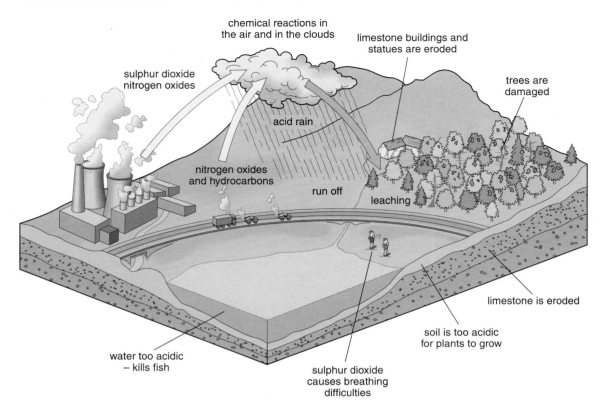

chemical reactions in the air and in the clouds

sulphur dioxide nitrogen oxides

limestone buildings and statues are eroded

trees are damaged

acid rain

nitrogen oxides and hydrocarbons

run off

leaching

limestone is eroded

soil is too acidic for plants to grow

water too acidic – kills fish

sulphur dioxide causes breathing difficulties

Acid rain has many damaging effects on wildlife, on natural rocks and building materials.

Acids in the air

When coal or oil are burned, the fumes include acidic gases, for example sulphur dioxide or nitrogen oxides. These react with water vapour in the air forming acids, so rain water is slightly acidic. You will learn more about this in the year 11 unit *Energy Today and Tomorrow*.

Acids in the air make iron rust faster.

Acids attack metals (SS) CM6

Acids attack metals. This is another reason why iron in buildings may corrode quickly.

When acids react with metals, they form salts, and hydrogen gas is given off, for example,

zinc + sulphuric acid → zinc sulphate + hydrogen
$Zn(s) + H_2SO_4(aq) \rightarrow ZnSO_4(aq) + H_2(g)$

Zinc + nitric acid → zinc nitrate + hydrogen
$Zn(s) + 2HNO_3(aq) \rightarrow Zn(NO_3)_2(aq) + H_2(g)$

F

Test for hydrogen gas: Hold a lighted splint to the gas. You will hear a squeaky 'pop' as the gas burns.

The test for hydrogen is to hold a lighted splint near the opening of a tube of the gas. If a 'popping' sound is heard, the gas is hydrogen.

Acids and building stone (SS) CM7

Look carefully at the buildings in your town. Many different types of rock are used in building.

Limestone and marble are popular types of building stone. They are two different forms of the same substance, calcium carbonate. They react with acids, forming carbon dioxide gas.

Calcium + hydrochloric → calcium + water + carbon
carbonate   acid   chloride   dioxide

$$CaCO_3 \;+\; 2HCl \;\rightarrow\; CaCl_2 + H_2O + CO_2$$

Test for carbon dioxide gas: Bubble the gas into lime-water. The lime-water goes cloudy.

You can investigate how fast limestone would wear away by collecting and measuring the carbon dioxide gas which is formed.

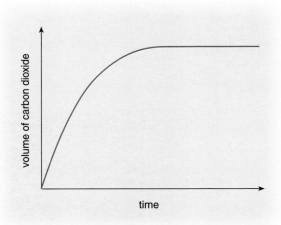

A graph to show how much gas is given off by the reaction as time goes on.

Things to do

1. Write formula equations for the reactions of
   a Magnesium (Mg)
   b Calcium (Ca)
   with sulphuric, hydrochloric and nitric acids.
2. Find out what the symbols (s), (aq) and (g) mean.

5 Fast or slow reactions?

Chemical reactions produce new substances. The substances put in at the start of the reaction are called **reactants**, the new substances made are called **products**.

Reactions happen when particles of the reactants collide with each other. For acid to dissolve limestone, acid particles must bump against the surface of the limestone.

Increasing the concentration

The more concentrated the acid, the closer together the particles are – so collisions happen more often

If the concentration of the acid is increased, there are more acid particles in the same volume of water.

Raising the temperature

If the acid is heated, the particles move faster.

At higher temperatures, collisions will be more frequent. Also, because of the higher speed, the particles have more energy, so the collisions are harder, and more of them will be effective in producing reaction.

If the acid is heated the particles move faster.

Making the surface area larger

If the limestone is crushed into smaller pieces, there will be a bigger surface exposed for the acid to bump into.

Both of these changes will make a chemical reaction go faster.

If the limestone is crushed, the surface area is bigger because more surface is exposed.

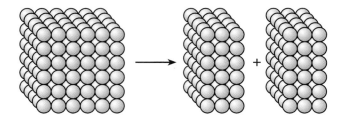

In each case, the acid particles collide with the limestone more frequently, and so the reaction will get faster.

F

Increasing the concentration of solutions makes reactions go faster.

Raising the temperature has a very big effect in making chemical reactions faster.

Increasing the surface area of solids (by grinding them up) makes reactions go faster.

Wheat grains don't burn easily, but finely powdered flour can cause explosions.

?

Things to do

This graph shows how fast carbon dioxide is made in a reaction between some lumps of limestone and 1.0M hydrochloric acid

Redraw the graph and sketch in the lines you would expect if:

1   the same mass of limestone powder was used (label this new line **A**)

2   the temperature was only 15 °C (line **B**)

3   only half the mass of limestone lumps was used, (label this line **C**).

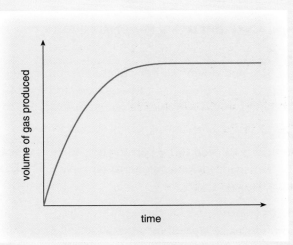

6 Renovating Hope Carr Barn

Hope Carr barn has been renovated and is now in use as a classroom and study centre. Here are some of the surveyor's recommendations for making good weather damage and preventing any new problems.

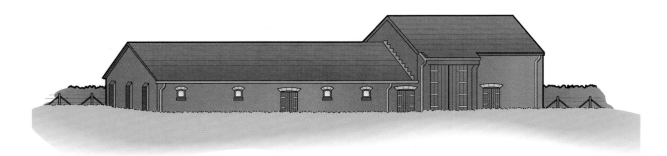

Hope Carr Barn, after renovation according to the surveyor's recommendations.

Smith and Smith Chartered Surveyors

Main Street, Kenwall, KS20 9QT

Hope Carr Barn: Surveyor's recommendations

Roof

To be stripped down. All defective timbers to be replaced with treated timber and covered with insulation and roofing felt. Missing slates to be replaced. Roof overhang to be increased to 14 cm. New gutters and downpipes in aluminium or PVC to be installed.

Walls

A second brick skin to be constructed, using stainless steel or galvanised wall ties, to form a cavity wall. Damaged brick and stone to be replaced. A damp-proof course to be installed to prevent further damage to brick.

Joinery

All timbers to be treated for infestation. All door frames to be constructed from treated pitch pine and painted. Windows to be replaced with plastic double-glazed units.

The survey report is very brief. The surveyor expected that the architect in charge would know about the chemical structure of each of the materials, and why each one was recommended.

1 Work in a group to make a poster about one of the materials which needs to be treated or replaced.

2 Use diagrams and notes to explain the structure of the material and how it is affected by weathering.

3 The damage could be repaired using the same traditional material or a newer material. Explain the advantages and disadvantages of each material which might be used. Remember to give as much detail of the chemical structure as possible.

Things to do

1 It is important not to let water penetrate into brickwork. Find an outside brick wall at your school, and make a list of all the ways in which it is protected against water penetration.

2 Here are some traditional building materials, and newer materials which could be used to replace them. Discuss with your group the advantages and disadvantages of each of the replacement materials.

Use	Traditional material	New material
Window frames	Wood	Aluminium or PVC
Gutters	Iron	Aluminium or PVC
Damp course	Slate	Plastic sheeting

3 Look at the picture. Write notes about the features which help to protect the house from damage by rainwater.

Buildings are designed and built to try to protect them from water damage.

1   Building sand is sold in plastic bags. It used to be sold in paper sacks.

a   Give one advantage and one disadvantage of using plastic bags instead of paper for sand.

b   Give some other examples to show where plastics have replaced other materials.

c   The plastic used for the bags is called polyethene. It is a thermoplastic polymer made by addition polymerisation. Explain what the terms 'thermoplastic' and 'addition polymerisation' mean.

2   Rubbish bags and the covers for electric plugs are both made from plastics.

a   Make a list of the ways in which the two plastics are similar. Make a separate list of the ways in which they are different.

b   Electrical plugs are made from a plastic made by condensation polymerisation, from monomer A and monomer B.
    If monomer A is

and monomer B is

what would be the name and the formula of the small molecule produced along with the polymer?

c   What are the differences between addition and condensation polymerisation?

3   This question is about clay and bricks.

a   Why is clay slippery and smooth when wet?

b   Explain why fired clay does not go slippery when it is wet.

c   Bricks are left to dry out thoroughly before being baked. Wet bricks explode if they are put into the kiln. Use ideas about particles to explain why this happens.

4   Iron rods are set into concrete to make it stronger. The concrete splits and cracks when the iron rusts.

a   Write an equation to show what happens when iron rusts. Explain why rusting is oxidation.

b   Suggest why the rusty iron makes the concrete crack.

c   Design an experiment to show that iron gains something from the air when it rusts.

d   Explain why using salt on icy roads can cause damage to concrete.

5   Use ideas you have learned in this unit to explain the following.

a   Iron hinges on bathroom and kitchen doors rust very quickly.

b   Galvanised iron does not rust even if the zinc coating is scratched.

c   Tin-coated iron cans rust faster than ordinary cans if the tin coating is scratched.

d   Electrical cables are made of copper wires coated with plastic – the copper stays shiny inside the plastic coating, but goes dull where the ends of the wire are not covered.

e   Magnesium powder is used to make fireworks, instead of magnesium ribbon.

f   If acid is spilled on your skin, drenching the spill with lots of water stops any damage.

INTRODUCING
Moving on

Forces affect the way we move about.

Try these first

1 Forces are always measured in:

   a kg   b Pa   c N.

2 Gravity pulls things towards the Earth.
   This force is called:

   a mass   b acceleration   c weight.

3 Byron's motorcycle takes him 150 m in 5 s.
   His speed is:

   a 150 m/s   b 30 m/s   c 5 m/s.

4 If the forces on it are as shown in this
   drawing, Byron's bike will:

   a slow down   b speed up
   c stay at the same speed.

400 N   200 N

In this unit you will learn:

- speed (m/s) = $\dfrac{\text{distance (m)}}{\text{time (s)}}$

- acceleration (m/s^2) = $\dfrac{\text{change of velocity (m/s)}}{\text{time taken (s)}}$

- force (N) = mass (kg) × acceleration (m/s^2)
- that velocity tells you speed *and* direction
- that unbalanced forces change velocities
- that counter forces act against driving forces
- that air resistance depends on speed
- how distance/time graphs can show us speed
- how velocity/time graphs can show us acceleration
- that forces are balanced at terminal velocity
- how safety belts, crumple zones and air-bags can reduce the forces on people in traffic accidents.

On your bike!

Forces affect the way things move. Single forces make things accelerate in the direction of the force. When you start a journey on a bicycle, the **driving force** you put on the pedals makes the bike **accelerate** (go faster).

How fast can you go? (SS) MO1, MO2

Even though you keep pedalling, your bike does not keep going faster and faster – why not? **Counter forces** (for example, air resistance) work against you.

As you cycle faster, the counter forces get bigger. Finally, they exactly balance the driving force. Then you go on at a steady speed.

When you stop pedalling, your bike slows down and stops. It seems as though you always need a continuous force to keep things moving. This is not always true.

The bike slows down because of forces like friction acting against its movement.

A bike has lots of counter forces acting on it, such as **air resistance**, **friction**, **weight** (if it goes uphill), **rolling resistance** from its tyres, and more rolling resistance from soft ground.

Driving forces try to speed things up.
Counter forces try to slow things down.

Driving and counter forces

Lots of different counter forces can act on a moving vehicle. The most common one is air resistance. As the speed increases, so does the air resistance. A more streamlined car has less air resistance at the same speed. Car makers measure the 'drag coefficient', in a wind tunnel. They try to design cars with a small drag coefficient. Cars like this use less fuel than cars with large drag coefficients at the same speed, and have a higher top speed when the air resistance is finally large enough to balance the driving force from the engine.

When a car goes uphill, part of its weight acts as a counter force. As the slope gets steeper the counter force gets bigger.

A streamlined shape means less air resistance...

...and therefore a smaller drag coefficient.

Rolling resistance on a car or bike includes friction in the wheels and axles as well as that from the tyres. Having the tyres at the correct pressure is very important. Soft tyres create more friction, can cause poor fuel consumption, and may make the steering dangerous. Tyres that are too hard will have less tread touching the road and this part will wear quickly making the tyre dangerous.

Adding forces (SS) M03, M04

Forces that are parallel can be added to find the single force that would replace them. If the forces are in opposite directions then you can subtract one from the other.

The single force that would replace the individual forces is usually called the **resultant.** The resultant force will be zero when the forces are balanced.

Putting the brakes on

Some counter forces are important for our safety! Car brakes have pads that rub on a disc fixed to the wheel. The friction forces make a large counter force to slow you down. Your bike brakes work in a similar way when the brake blocks rub on the rim.

Some other counter forces are noticed most when they aren't there! Have you ever been standing on a bus that stopped suddenly? You are moving forward, and unless there is a counter force to stop you, your body continues to move forward even when the bus stops. This happens because the bus has a counter force to slow it down, and you don't.

To keep the counter force small, roads usually 'zig-zag' up steep hills instead of going straight up.

Friction can be annoying at times, but in car and bike brakes it's essential!

? Things to do

1 a Find the resultant force in each picture.

   b How will the movement of each object be changing as a result of these forces?

2 a Which of the two cars in the photographs opposite will have the smallest drag coefficient?

   b Which do you think will have the highest top speed? Explain how air resistance affects this.

3 When a car is not moving, the resultant force on it will be _____ . At its top speed the resultant will be _____ .

4 A car is travelling at its top speed. Its weight is 13 000 N and the driving force is 3000 N. Draw a diagram and mark on it the four forces that you know.

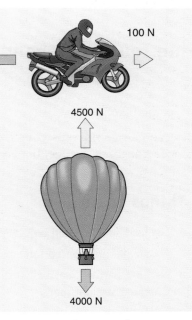

600 N

100 N

4500 N

4000 N

Why can't I go faster?

When you ride your bike, you make a driving force by pushing on the pedals. As you go faster, air resistance increases with speed until it is equal and opposite to your driving force. The resultant force is then zero and you will travel at a constant speed. You have reached **terminal velocity**. You can't go faster unless you make the driving force bigger or the air resistance smaller.

On Earth, there are always forces, such as air resistance or friction or weight, which make it harder to predict how an object will move. In space, there is no air, so no air-resistance. A spaceship would not need its engine to keep moving at a steady speed.

This cyclist is making the air resistance as small as possible. He will still reach a terminal velocity – but it will be a faster one than yours!

Newton's First Law

Sir Isaac Newton worked out a law that lets you predict how an object will move, however many forces are acting.

Newton's First Law tells us that an object with no forces on it (or one with balanced forces on it) will either stay at rest (not moving) or carry on at the same speed in a straight line.

The unit of force is named after Sir Isaac Newton – forces are measured in newtons (N).

Velocity means speed in a particular direction.

On some cycle journeys, you pedal steadily, so your speed doesn't change. But if you go round bends, then your velocity does change.

Forces can make things go faster, or slower, or change direction.

Unbalanced forces cause a change in velocity.

Going round the bend

In order to change direction, an unbalanced force is needed. If you want to go round a corner on your bike, you lean over – this makes a sideways force on the bike.

Forces can change not only your speed, but also which way you are going! Your speed may not change, but your direction does.

Things to do

1   What happens to an object when the forces on it are balanced?

2   A single, unbalanced force on an object will change its _____ or its _____ .

3   With a partner, make a list of all the different forces acting when you cycle at a steady speed along a straight road.

Distance/time graphs

In the graph of the motorcyclist's journey, the line slopes up to the right because as time passes, the distance travelled gets greater. The line is straight because the rider is going at a steady speed.

$$\text{speed} = \frac{\text{distance travelled}}{\text{time taken}}$$

The motor cyclist travels 150 m in 5 s. The average speed is $\frac{150}{5}$ = 30 m/s.

The gradient of the line shows the speed – the faster the movement, the steeper the line.

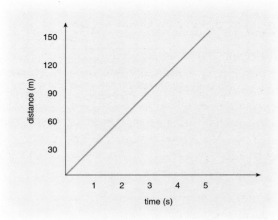

This graph shows the distance travelled by a motorcyclist travelling steadily along a motorway.

Real journeys are more complicated!

On some graphs there will be sections with different gradients as the speed changes. If the line is parallel to the 'time' axis, it means that the distance isn't changing at all: the speed is zero!

This graph shows how the distance from the start changed over time for a short car journey. Notice that some parts of this graph are curved. What does this mean? A curve shows that the speed is changing. Change of speed is called acceleration.

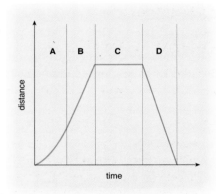

A distance/time graph for a car journey.

? Things to do

1 Look at the graph above, showing a short car journey.
   Describe what is happening in each stage **A**, **B**, **C** and **D** of the journey.

2 Ann travels 270 km to York in 3 hours
   a What is her average speed in km/h?
   b What is this in m/s?

3 The table shows the distance travelled by a lorry at different times during a journey.

Time (h)	0	1	2	3	4	5
Distance (km)	0	40	80	130	180	210

Plot a distance/time graph for this journey. Use straight lines to join the points. Calculate the average speed shown on each section of the graph.

One thing that everybody knows about movement is that things fall down!

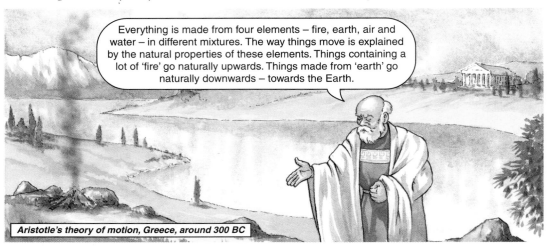

Everything is made from four elements – fire, earth, air and water – in different mixtures. The way things move is explained by the natural properties of these elements. Things containing a lot of 'fire' go naturally upwards. Things made from 'earth' go naturally downwards – towards the Earth.

Aristotle's theory of motion, Greece, around 300 BC

According to Aristotle's ideas, heavier objects would fall faster than light ones. The speed of fall would be proportional to the density of the object.

Greek philosophers relied mainly on observations of the world around them. The idea of setting up experiments to test ideas came later.

I think that all heavy solid objects fall through the air at exactly the same rate, no matter how heavy they are.

See, the one-kilogram mass and the ten-kilogram mass reach the ground at the same time.

But *how* do things fall?

This is only a legend

Galileo's demonstration experiment, Italy, around 1600 AD

Well, I think falling objects get faster by the same amount each second.

They accelerate uniformly. So the distance an object falls will increase as the square of the time. If you drop any heavy object, you'll find that it falls 5m in 1 second. After 2 seconds it will have fallen 20m – four times as far (four is two squared – the square of the time). After 3 seconds, it will have fallen 45m – nine times as far. And so on.

Galileo's ideas were also based on observation of things around him, but in addition he tried to test his ideas by setting up experiments. If the results of an experiment matched his predictions, his ideas may have been right.

Why do things fall down?

All objects are attracted towards each other. The force that pulls objects towards each other is called **gravity**. Gravity acts on every object, on Earth and throughout the Universe.

Because the Earth is such a massive object, everything on Earth is pulled towards it. Things tend to fall straight down (towards the centre of the Earth). The force of gravity on an object is called its weight.

F

Mass is the amount of matter an object is made of. It is always the same, wherever the object is.

Weight is the force of gravity on the object.

This astronaut has a mass of 70 kg on Earth, in space or on the Moon.

The astronaut weighs 700 N on Earth, about 120 N on the Moon, and nothing in space!

More thinking about gravity

Most people accepted Aristotle's ideas about gravity until about 1600 AD when Galileo suggested that all objects are accelerated down towards the Earth at the same rate. What sort of test could you do to decide between these theories?

Gravity is always there

If you drop a ball, it falls, getting faster and faster. The force that accelerates it downwards is its weight.

If you put the ball on a table, it stays still. Gravity is still pulling the ball down, but the force is balanced by the table pushing up on the ball. (This is called a **reaction force**.)

How does the table make this upward force? Think what would happen if you put the ball on a piece of foam. The foam would be squeezed down. The foam is springy so would push up on the ball. The ball sinks in until the upward force exactly equals the weight of the ball.

The table top is not squeezed as easily as the foam, but it is compressed by the ball, until the forces are equal and opposite. It's just that the compression is not large enough for you to see.

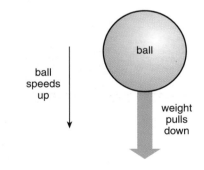

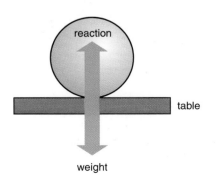

Here is a way to show that things accelerate as they fall – that is, they fall faster and faster, not just at the same speed all the way.

Take two threads and tie five buttons on each, at the positions shown. Hold each thread so that the bottom just touches a table. Drop one thread, then the other.

If the threads fall at constant speed, the sound of buttons landing should be equally spread for thread 2. If the thread falls faster and faster, the sounds will be equally spread for thread 1.

What is acceleration?

Acceleration is a measure of how quickly velocity is changing. You need quite a lot of information to calculate acceleration:

- how fast the object was going at the beginning of the time
- how fast it is going at the end of the time
- how long the change has taken.

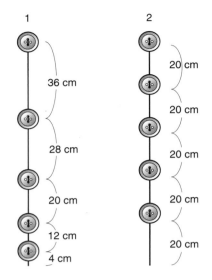

Because the buttons fall faster and faster, the buttons on thread 1 seem to land at regular intervals, even though they are not evenly spaced.

F

$$\text{acceleration} = \frac{\text{change in velocity}}{\text{time taken}}$$

For example, manufacturers compare the performances of different cars by giving the time it takes for each car to accelerate from a standing start to 60 mph. The Ford Mondeo 1.8LX can reach 60 mph in 10 seconds, so its average acceleration is $\frac{60}{10}$ = 6 mph per second.

Check that you understand what acceleration really means. If a train accelerates from standing, at 0.5 m/s²:

- at the start its speed is 0 m/s
- after 1 second its speed is 0.5 m/s
- after 2 seconds its speed is 1.0 m/s
- after 3 seconds its speed is 1.5 m/s and so on.

When things slow down, the speed gets smaller. The acceleration is given a negative sign to show this.

Acceleration and gravity

One way to measure how things accelerate as they fall is to use a light gate and a computer timer. Drop a 'C' shaped card like this one through the light gate.

If you tell the computer the length of each side piece, its program can work out the two speeds and the time between the two side pieces reaching the light gate. The program can now work out the acceleration.

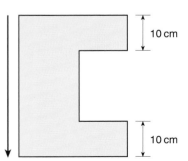

As the card falls, each side piece briefly blocks the light. The computer can measure the time for each side piece to pass the light gate.

Velocity/time graphs

Velocity/time graphs show how fast something moves at each stage in a journey.

If the line is sloping, it shows that the speed is changing; that is, the object is accelerating. The greater the acceleration, the steeper the graph.

You can find the acceleration from a velocity/time graph by measuring its slope. Find the velocity at the end of the section of graph you are investigating, and at the beginning. Subtract to find the *change* in velocity.

Find the time at the beginning and at the end of the section and subtract to find the time taken. Now divide the change in velocity by the time taken to find the acceleration.

In part **A** of this graph (the first part of the journey), the speed goes from 0 to 30 m/s.

change in speed = 30 − 0 = 30 m/s

time taken = 4 s

acceleration $= \dfrac{\text{change in speed}}{\text{time}}$

$= \dfrac{30}{4} = 7.5$ m/s²

Look at part **B** of the graph. The line is horizontal. What does this tell you about the speed of the motorcycle during this stage of the journey? (Hint – this is the main part of the journey, when the bike is travelling steadily.)

What do you think is happening during the stage of the journey shown by part C of the graph? Calculate the average acceleration during part C of the journey.

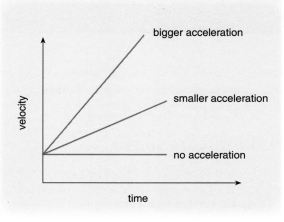

The slope of a velocity/time graph tells you about the acceleration.

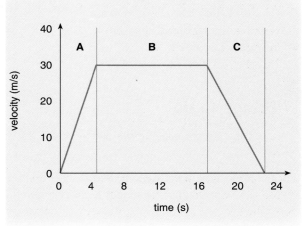

This graph shows the speed of a motorcyclist during a journey.

Things to do

1   a A runner accelerates smoothly from 5 m/s to 7 m/s in 2 s. What is his acceleration?

   b If he continues to accelerate at the same rate for another second, how fast will he be running?

2   A car travelling at 20 m/s accelerates to overtake a lorry. After 5 s, it is doing 30 m/s. What was the average acceleration?

3   A lorry travelling at 18 m/s takes 3 s to stop when the brakes are put on. What is its (negative) acceleration?

4   Anita spends 30 s walking to the bus stop at 2 m/s. She waits 1 min for the bus. The bus travels at a steady 10 m/s for 3 min. As soon as Anita gets off the bus, she hurries into school at 3 m/s. This stage of her journey takes 90 s.

   a Plot a velocity/time graph for this journey.

   b Work out the distance that Anita travelled on the bus.

Balanced forces do not change movement. Unbalanced forces on an object will cause acceleration. Does the size of the unbalanced force make any difference to the acceleration?

Making cars move

Have you ever been asked to help push a broken-down car? If so, you will know how much better it is if you can get other people to help, and so make a bigger **driving force**.

When cars are working properly, the driving force comes from the engine. What difference does engine size make? Look at this information from a car maker. All of the cars have the same body size and shape, but they have different sized engines.

Model	Engine size (cc)	Time 0–60 mph (s)	Average acceleration (mph/s)
Mondeo 1.6 LX	1598	12.9	
Mondeo 1.8 LX	1796	10.2	
Mondeo 2.0 LX	1989	9.2	
Mondeo 24 V	2544	7.7	

Things to do

1 Copy out the table above and work out the average acceleration for each car.

2 Draw a graph of engine size (*x*-axis) against acceleration (*y*-axis). Do the results show a pattern?

3 How clear is the pattern? Are all the results exactly in line? If not, what other factors, apart from engine size, might be having an effect?

Linking force and acceleration MO8

As with most things in real life, the results for the cars in the table don't give a perfect pattern because lots of other factors can affect the results. In order to be sure about the effect of force on acceleration, it is necessary to do experiments in which all other factors are controlled.

You can use an investigation with light gates.

A C-shaped double card is fixed on a trolley. The trolley is accelerated by a weight pulling on the thread. The computer measures the time for each section of the card to pass the light gate. You need to enter the length of each section of the card into the computer, which can then work out the speed of each. It also measures the time between the two side pieces passing the light gate, and it can then work out the acceleration.

You can use equipment like this to measure the effects of force on acceleration.

For each test, note the force (weight on the thread) and the acceleration that is produced. To make this a fair test, always use the same trolley on the same track.

You have to be very careful with this investigation! As the trolley moves, everything that is moving is being accelerated. This includes the string and the hanging weight. If you add extra weights, you will change the mass being accelerated, and so affect the results!

So, where should you keep the spare weights? Put them on the trolley! Then for each experiment, you can simply move some of the weights from the trolley onto the end of the string. In this way, you will get a different force on the string, but keep the total moving mass constant.

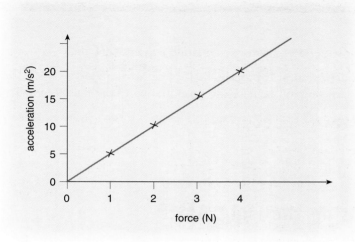

The graph is straight, which shows that the acceleration is directly proportional to the force.

 If the mass stays the same, the acceleration produced is directly proportional to the force.

Linking mass and acceleration (SS) M09

Does the mass of the trolley make a difference? You can find out using the light gate apparatus again. Keep the same weight on the string for all the experiments, so that the accelerating force is always the same.

Measure the total mass of the trolley, plus the string, plus the hanging mass. Measure the acceleration as many times as necessary to get a reliable result.

Now pile extra weights on the trolley, calculate the new total mass, and again measure the acceleration. Repeat this to get results for a good range of total masses. Here are some sample results:

Total mass (g)	200	400	600	800	1000
Acceleration (cm/s^2)	12.0	6.0	4.0	3.0	2.4

Notice that if the mass is bigger, the acceleration produced by the force is less. If you double the mass, the acceleration is halved. Three times the mass gives one-third of the acceleration.
This is an **inverse proportion**.

 If the force stays the same, the acceleration is inversely proportional to the mass.

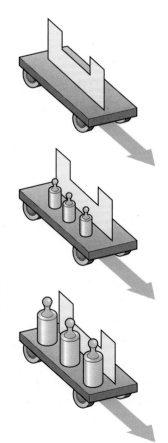

In this experiment, you change the total mass of the trolley, and see if that affects acceleration.

6 Force, mass and acceleration

We have seen, from two separate experiments, that:

● acceleration is proportional to the force applied
● acceleration is inversely proportional to the mass being accelerated.

These two results can be put together to show how all three quantities are linked:

force = mass × acceleration
F = ma

Using the right units

The first person to work out and publish this link between force, mass and acceleration was Sir Isaac Newton. It is called Newton's Second Law of Motion, and the unit used for force is called the **newton** (N).

A force of 1 newton (N) will give an acceleration of 1 metre per second per second (m/s²) to a mass of 1 kilogram (kg).

You will only get the right answer in your calculations if you are careful to use the right units for all of the quantities!

Working out accelerations

To calculate the average acceleration, first convert the speed from mph to metres per second:

1 mile   = 1600 metres
60 miles = 60 × 1600 = 96 000 metres
1 hour   = 60 minutes = 60 × 60 seconds
         = 3600 seconds

∴ speed in m/s $= \dfrac{96\ 000}{3600} = 26.7$ m/s

change in speed = (final − initial speed)
= 26.7 − 0 = 26.7 m/s

acceleration = $\dfrac{\text{change in speed}}{\text{time taken}} = \dfrac{26.7}{10.5} = 2.5$ m/s²

The total mass of Bobby's car (with Bobby in it!) is 1200 kg. The handbook says the car will accelerate from 0 to 60 mph in 10.5 s.

To work out the average force from the engine during the acceleration:

mass of the vehicle (plus driver) = 1200 kg
acceleration = 2.5 m/s²

force (N) = mass (kg) × acceleration (m/s²)
force   = 1200 × 2.5 = 3000 N

?

Things to do

1   Use leaflets from car manufacturers to find the mass of different models and the time from 0–60 mph. Work out the average force from the engine for each model.

How much will it hurt? MO12

If you are involved in a collision when cycling or in a car, your velocity changes suddenly. (Only dummies should drive into walls!)

You can use Newton's Second Law of Motion to work out what would happen to you if you were involved in a collision.

force = mass × acceleration

$$F = ma$$

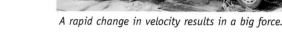

A rapid change in velocity results in a big force.

You also know that acceleration equals change in velocity/time, so:

$$\text{force} = \text{mass} \times \frac{\text{change in velocity}}{\text{time}}$$

$$F = \frac{m\,(v_1 - v_2)}{t}$$

In this case, the mass is your mass, and the time is the time from the beginning of the collision until you finally stop. So, if you can spread out the time it takes to stop, the force on you will be smaller. Crumple zones on cars, seat belts and air-bags are all designed to spread collisions over longer times and so reduce injuries.

Crumple zones

Look at the photograph of the crash-test car, above. Notice how the front of the car has crumpled in the collision, but the passenger compartment is not damaged.

Both the front and the rear of cars are made so that in a collision they will be steadily crushed, so slowing the car more gradually. These 'crumple zones' spread the collision over a longer time and so reduce the force on the passengers.

Design your own crumple zone! Use a heavy trolley (tape a brick or weight to the trolley) on a sloping ramp. Use card, paper or tissues for the crumple zone. If your zone is too soft (or too hard) it won't work!

During the development of new models of cars, test cars are crashed into walls to make sure the crumple zones work properly.

Crash helmets

This same idea is used in cycle helmets made from polystyrene foam with a thin hard plastic shell on the outside. In an accident the foam is crushed so the force on the wearer's head is made smaller. The helmet would then need to be replaced as the foam will have been permanently damaged. Modern car bumpers are made in the same way.

A cycle helmet could save your life in an accident, by reducing the force on your head.

Why use seat belts? (SS) M013

In head-on crashes, there are often two collisions, not just one. The first is when the car hits an obstruction and stops. The people inside carry on moving (objects continue in a straight line with constant velocity unless a force acts on them). The second collision happens when they crash into the windscreen!

Seat belts are designed to provide a force that will hold you in your seat. The pictures on the left are taken from a film that shows what happened in a test crash. As the crash begins, the car stops, but the driver continues to move forward. This begins to stretch the seat belt, causing a force that gradually slows the driver down and stops him before he hits the steering wheel. Notice that seat belts are designed to stretch a little, so that you slow down gradually, and this reduces the force you feel.

These pictures show the results of four other crash tests, with and without seat belts.

?

Things to do

1   Look at the pictures showing four crash tests, with and without seat belts. What differences can you see between

    a Tests 1 and 2   **b** Tests 3 and 4?

2   How can seat belts for rear seat passengers help to reduce injuries to:

    a rear seat passengers   **b** front seat passengers?

Do you really need to wear your seat belt? Except at very low speeds, you cannot possibly save yourself from being thrown about by a collision if you are not using a seat belt.

Without the seat belt, this driver's head could have been crushed on the steering wheel during the collision.

A soft cushion to land on

Air-bags in cars give extra protection in collisions.

Front air-bags are fitted in the steering wheel or in the dashboard. The shock of a front-end collision sets off a reaction in a chemical inside the bag.

The reaction very quickly forms a large volume of gas (it is really a small explosion!). The gas fills the bag, which holds you in your seat.

The bag is porous and goes down quickly after the accident.

Air-bags are only set off if the collision speed is over 30 km/h. Even with an air-bag, this would be very unpleasant!

Notice that seat belts depend on you – you may forget to put yours on. Air-bags work automatically.

An air-bag provides extra cushioning to protect you in a collision.

Things to do

3   Convert 30 km/h into a speed in m/s.

4   From the time a driver hits the air-bag, it takes 0.03 s for the car to stop. What is the average acceleration?

5   If the driver has a mass of 70 kg, what is the average force from the air-bag?

6   Why are air-bags designed to go down quickly after an accident?

F

In this unit you have learned a lot of new ideas. Here are some of the most important ones:

- Speed (m/s) = distance (m)/time (s).
- Forces are measured in newtons. They can push, pull, twist or turn things.
- Newton's First Law tells us that an object with no forces on it (or one with balanced forces on it) will either stay at rest or carry on at the same speed in a straight line.
- Forces that are parallel can be added. The total is called the resultant.
- Velocity is the speed in a particular direction.
- If an object has an unbalanced force acting on it, its velocity will change.
- Acceleration (m/s^2) = change in velocity (m/s)/time taken (s).
- If the mass stays the same then the force is proportional to the acceleration.
- If the force stays the same then the acceleration is inversely proportional to the mass.
- Newton's Second Law tells us that force (N) = mass (kg) × acceleration (m/s^2).
- If an object is stopped in a longer time the forces on it are smaller.
- Crumple zones make forces on car passengers smaller.
- Seat belts provide a bigger restraining force to stop you before you hit the windscreen.
- We can find the velocity from a distance/time graph by finding the gradient.
- A distance/time graph with a steeper line is showing a faster speed.
- If a distance/time graph is straight it is showing constant speed.
- We can find the acceleration from a velocity/time graph by finding its gradient.
- If a velocity/time graph is straight it is showing constant acceleration.

1 a   A cyclist in the Tour de France rides 180 km in 4.5 h.

   b   What is his average speed in km/h?

   c   What is his average speed in m/s?

2   A sprinter runs 100 m in 10 s. What is his average speed?

3   A train travels 120 km in 40 min. What is its speed in:

   a   m/min

   b   m/s?

4   A cyclist sets off down hill on a long straight road without pedalling. Explain carefully what will happen to his speed (hint – think about the forces on him).

5   Find the resultant of the forces in the following:

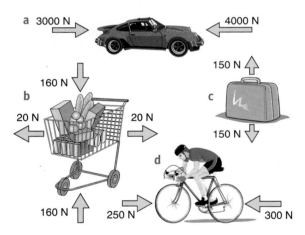

a 3000 N → ← 4000 N

b 160 N ↓   20 N ←   → 20 N   160 N ↑

c 150 N ↑   150 N ↓

d 250 N → ← 300 N

6   Look carefully at the graph. It shows the journey of a cyclist riding on a straight road.

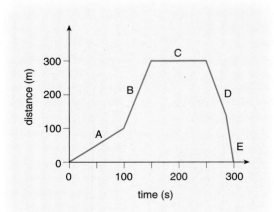

a   What do you think is happening in part C?

b   When is the cyclist travelling fastest? How do you know?

c   Work out her speed in each stage of the ride.

d   One part of the ride is up hill. Which is it?

7   A car accelerates from 20 m/s to 30 m/s in 5s. What is its acceleration?

8   James has a small powered scooter, which gets from 4 m/s to 10 m/s in 5 s.

   a   If James and the scooter have a total mass of 60 kg, what is the force provided by the motor?

   b   When he brakes what do you think will happen to the kinetic (movement) energy?

9   A bonfire night rocket travels 120 m up into the air in 2 s.

   a   What is its average speed?

   b   Describe what you think happens to the rocket during its journey. When do you think it will:

   i   travel fastest

   ii   have a velocity of 0 m/s

   iii accelerate

   iv   have a negative acceleration?

10 A cyclist has a mass of 60 kg and accelerates at 0.5 m/s². What is the force on her?

11 A bullet travels down the barrel of a gun in 0.05 s.

   a   If it leaves the barrel at 350 m/s, what is the acceleration along the barrel?

   b   If the bullet has a mass of 10 g what is the force on it?

12 a   Write down three important ways in which injuries to car passengers in an accident can be reduced.

   b   Choose one of them and explain carefully why the forces on the passenger become smaller.

INTRODUCING
Food for thought

Try these first

1 The first organism in a food chain is always:

   a the Sun   b a plant   c an animal.

2 Arrange these to make an equation for photosynthesis:

   carbon dioxide   oxygen   glucose   water

3 Which of these can reduce the yield of food from a farm?

   a bees   b weeds   c irrigation

4 Which of these elements is needed for healthy plant growth?

   a lead   b sodium   c nitrogen

In this unit you will learn:

- how fertilisers can help plant growth
- which elements are needed by plants
- how ammonia and ammonium salts are made
- about conditions that affect reversible chemical reactions
- about the importance of controlling soil acidity
- how herbicides and pesticides are used
- about the importance of protecting food in storage
- how enzymes are used in food processing
- how yeast is used in making alcoholic drinks and in bread-making.

People use many methods to grow more food crops.

The world food problem (SS) FT1

You probably take it for granted that there will be something for tea tonight. But we see from television reports that many people in the world are starving, though organisations like Oxfam work hard to help them. The world's population is increasing rapidly. To keep pace, we need to grow more crops, and find ways of reducing the amount of food lost because of plant diseases, pests or spoilage in storage.

Improving crop growth (SS) FT2

Plants use water and carbon dioxide to make sugars and starch in a process called **photosynthesis**. They can use the sugar to make all the other chemicals they need; for example, chlorophyll for photosynthesis, and proteins for cell membranes. These conversions often also involve nutrients, which the plant obtains from the soil, through its roots. Nitrates are one of these **nutrients** and they are vital for protein synthesis.

As plants grow, they take in nutrients, so the amounts left in the soil get smaller. If the plants are left to rot back into the soil, bacteria can recycle the nutrients. If crops are removed, this recycling cannot happen and the soil gradually gets less and less fertile. Chemicals that are added to the soil to replace nutrients are called **fertilisers**. Sometimes **natural** fertilisers like manure or compost are spread on the soil; sometimes **manufactured** (inorganic) fertilisers are used.

Inorganic fertilisers replace lost nitrogen phosphorus and potassium salts in the s...

Ways of improving crop production

making better use of lands such as deserts or marshes

using chemicals, such as pesticides and fertilisers

making more use of machines for farming and transport

using better adapted varieties of plants, such as winter wheat

making available supplies of water

We can get more crops from the land available in many different ways.

Inorganic fertilisers (SS) FT3

The main elements in manufactured fertilisers are:

- nitrogen (N) as nitrates or ammonium salts
- phosphorus (P) as phosphates
- potassium (K) as potassium salts.

Nitrogen is the mineral element needed in largest amounts by cereal crops.

The right fertiliser for the right crop

In one of the longest experiments ever carried out, potatoes and wheat were grown on land treated with controlled amounts of fertiliser each year. The figures in the table show the amount of fertiliser spread on each hectare. (A hectare (ha) is an area measuring 100 metres by 100 metres.)

Amount of fertiliser used each year (kg/ha)			Crop yield (tonnes/ha)	
N	P	K	wheat	potatoes
0	0	0	1.69	8.47
96	0	0	3.68	8.30
0	77	107	2.04	16.63
96	77	107	6.60	38.57

If any of the major nutrients is in limited supply, it slows the whole range of chemical reactions inside plant cells that lead to healthy plant growth.

How much fertiliser should you use?

Farmers have to work out very carefully the best dose of fertiliser to use. This is important not only because fertilisers are expensive, but also because they are easily leached (washed out of the soil) into nearby waterways. You can read more about this in *Balancing acts*.

Amount of nitrogen fertiliser (kg/ha)	Yield of grain (tonnes/ha)
0	4.0
50	5.9
100	7.3
150	8.4
200	8.9
250	9.0
300	8.7

? Things to do

1 Look at the table showing how the amount of fertiliser used affects crop yield for wheat and potatoes.

   a Explain the effect of adding nitrogen fertiliser *only* to land used for growing:

   i wheat   ii potatoes.

   b Which crop shows the biggest increase in yield when potassium and phosphorus fertilisers are used?

2 Look at the table showing how the amount of nitrogen fertiliser used affects grain yield.

   a Draw a graph to show how the amount of grain harvested is related to the amount of fertiliser used.

   b How many extra tonnes of grain would come from a 1 hectare field as a result of adding 50 kg of nitrogen fertiliser:

   i if no fertiliser had been used before   ii if 200 kg of fertiliser had already been used?

3 Look at the labels on bags of fertilisers in shops or garden centres. List the nutrients mentioned.

4 Explain why growing and harvesting crops will gradually result in the soil becoming infertile.

As plants grow, they are surrounded by nitrogen in the air – but it is so unreactive that they cannot use it. Making nitrogen react to form a compound that plants can use is called 'fixing' the nitrogen. About 100 years ago, a German chemist called Fritz Haber invented a method of making nitrogen from the air combine with hydrogen to form ammonia.

Notice the symbol $\rightleftharpoons$ in the equation on the right. It shows that the reaction is **reversible**. To understand the difficulties this caused for Haber, we need to know something about reversible reactions.

$$N_2 + 3H_2 \rightleftharpoons 2NH_3$$

Reversible reactions

Most chemical equations show **reactants** on the left and **products** on the right.

reactants → products

The reactants are used up completely and changed into products. It is not possible to make the process work in the opposite direction.

A **reversible reaction** can be made to 'go' in either direction, depending on the conditions.

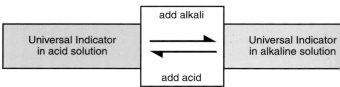

Usually, very extreme conditions are needed to make the reaction complete in either direction. More often, a stage is reached where the reaction is only partially complete, but no more product is formed. We say the reaction has reached **equilibrium**.

The reaction of an indicator to show acids or alkalis is a good example of a reversible reaction.

The main factors that affect how far a reversible reaction will go are temperature, and pressure (for gases) or concentration (for solutions).

A reversible reaction happens when we heat copper sulphate crystals. You may have seen this reaction.

The crystals are blue, and they contain water, chemically linked to the copper sulphate. When they are heated, the water is driven out. The crystals turn to white powder, and we see drops of water near the top of the test tube. If we add water to the white powder, it turns back to blue again. The reaction is reversed.

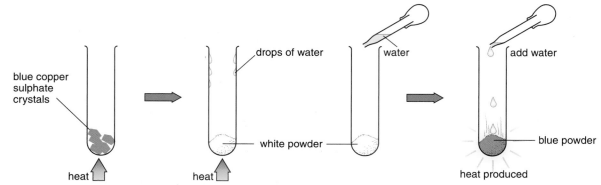

This reversible reaction is used as a test for water.

Separating the water from copper sulphate takes in heat energy – the reaction is **endothermic**. When water is added again, heat is given out and the copper sulphate gets very hot. The reverse reaction is **exothermic** (heat is given out). For all reversible reactions, if the reaction is exothermic in one direction, it will be endothermic in the other. The energy change is reversed, as well as the chemical change.

Making the Haber process work

Haber faced great difficulties making his process work on a commercial scale. By 1913, an engineer, Carl Bosch, finally succeeded.

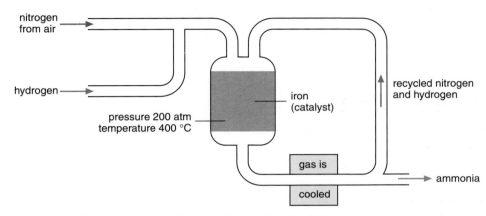

To get the Haber process to work you need to use just the right conditions of pressure and temperature, and a catalyst too.

Choosing the right pressure

Increasing the pressure on gases squashes the particles of gas closer together. At any given temperature, the greater the pressure the more ammonia will be formed. Bosch and Haber built reaction chambers so strong they could stand a pressure of 200 atmospheres (that is, 200 times the pressure of the atmosphere – more than the pressure of an elephant standing on one foot!).

Getting the temperature right

You may have noticed that the formula for nitrogen is N_2, and the formula for hydrogen is H_2. In these gases, the atoms are linked together in pairs. A reaction can only happen if the particles collide hard enough to break these links, so that the atoms are free to react. At room temperature, the gases do not react. If the mixture of hydrogen and nitrogen is heated, collisions between particles become more frequent and more violent. The higher the temperature, the faster the reaction will go.

Unfortunately, if the temperature is too high, the particles collide so hard that the ammonia molecules are broken into nitrogen and hydrogen again! Bosch and Haber needed to find just the right temperature. Most modern works use a temperature of about 400 °C.

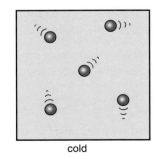
cold

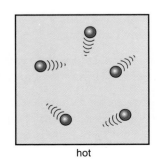
hot

When the temperature is higher, the particles move more quickly.

3 Ammonia reacts with acids

Catalysts make things quicker!

Even at 400°C, the reaction was too slow, until Bosch and Haber discovered that pieces of iron metal in the reaction chamber made it go faster. Something that makes a chemical reaction faster, without changing the final result, is called a **catalyst**. Passing the gases across many small pieces of iron gave a large surface for contact and made the reaction much faster.

Things to do

1 Find iron in the Periodic Table. It is one of a large family of metals called transition metals. Many of these are useful catalysts in industrial processes. Try to find some other examples of transition metals being used as catalysts.

2 This table shows the percentage of hydrogen and nitrogen converted to ammonia under different conditions (if the reaction could be left long enough to reach equilibrium).

Pressure (atm)	Percentage of hydrogen and nitrogen converted to ammonia (%)		
	100°C	300°C	500°C
50	94.5	39.5	5.6
100	96.7	52.5	10.6
200	98.4	66.7	18.3
400	99.4	79.7	31.9

a Draw a graph to show these results. Estimate the percentage conversion at 400°C and 200 atm.

b Discuss what factors affect the choice of temperature and pressure for the process.

Making ammonium salts FT6

Ammonia is an alkaline gas. It dissolves in water to form an alkaline solution. Ammonia can be used as a fertiliser but it would change the pH of the soil. Many plants only grow well in particular pH conditions. So it would be better if a fertiliser did not alter the soil pH. In addition, ammonia is a very unpleasant smelly gas. High concentrations of it in the air would be extremely dangerous.

If ammonia is reacted with an acid it forms a **salt**. Salts are solids and have almost neutral pH. Ammonium salts have several advantages as fertilisers:

- solids are easier to handle than gases
- there is no smelly gas to escape into the air
- salts are not so quickly dissolved and washed away as ammonia gas
- the effect on soil pH is easier to control.

F

A test for ammonia is that it turns litmus or universal indicator blue.

Reactions between acids and bases are called **neutralisations**:

base + acid → salt + water

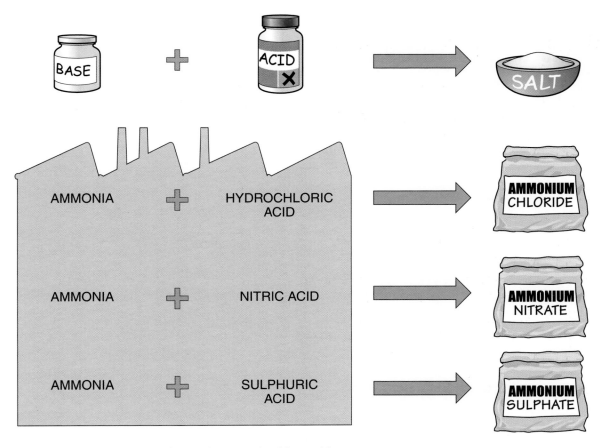

Ammonium salts are made by reacting ammonia with an acid.

Naming salts

The name of a salt is chosen to show which acid and base it can be made from.

All acids contain hydrogen. Salts are formed when hydrogen in the acid is replaced by metals or ammonia. The name of the salt formed depends on the acid used and the chemical that replaces the hydrogen.

The picture shows the names of three ammonium salts that are very important as fertilisers. Their formulas are:

- ammonium chloride, NH_4Cl
- ammonium nitrate, NH_4NO_3
- ammonium sulphate, $(NH_4)_2SO_4$.

Manufacturing fertilisers (SS) FT8

Ammonium nitrate is used in very large amounts as a fertiliser. Ammonia manufactured in the Haber process is reacted with nitric acid to form ammonium nitrate, which is dried to produce small pellets. These are bagged up and sold as a 'straight' fertiliser. Sometimes the pellets are mixed with ammonium phosphate and potassium chloride to form a 'compound' fertiliser or NPK fertiliser.

Things to do

1 Write word equations and balanced symbol equations for the formation of ammonium nitrate, ammonium chloride and ammonium sulphate.

2 Ammonium phosphate is also used in fertilisers.

   a Which acid reacts with ammonia to form ammonium phosphate?

   b Find the formula of ammonium phosphate in a chemical catalogue. Apart from nitrogen, which other useful plant nutrient does it contain?

Making sulphuric acid

Another very commonly used fertiliser is ammonium sulphate. It is made by reacting ammonia with sulphuric acid. The sulphuric acid is made in the Contact process using the raw materials sulphur, air and water.

Look at the flow diagram to see how these raw materials are converted into sulphuric acid.

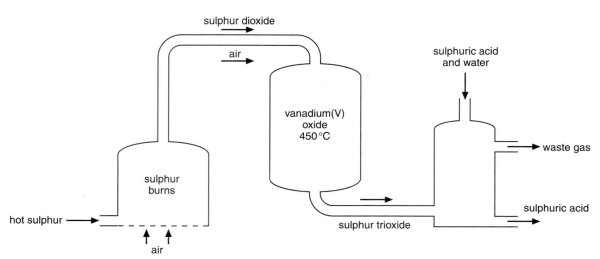

The Contact process.

Stages in the Contact process

This process can be divided into three stages.

1 Sulphur is burned in air to form sulphur dioxide gas:

$$S + O_2 \rightarrow SO_2$$

2 The sulphur dioxide and air are passed over a heated catalyst. This forms sulphur trioxide:

$$2SO_2 + O_2 \rightarrow 2SO_3$$

The catalyst is vanadium(V) oxide. Vanadium is a transition metal and makes an excellent catalyst.

3 Sulphur trioxide is passed through a mixture of 98% sulphuric acid and 2% water. The sulphur trioxide reacts with the water to form sulphuric acid:

$$SO_3 + H_2O \rightarrow H_2SO_4$$

Not all the sulphuric acid produced is used for fertiliser manufacture. It is a very important chemical in its own right. Look at the picture and see some of the many different uses of sulphuric acid.

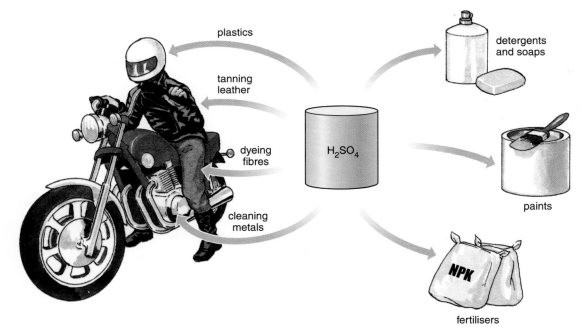

Sulphuric acid is used to manufacture many useful products.

Working out reacting masses

Fertiliser factories need to know how much of each chemical to use for a batch of fertiliser. They use the chemical equation for the reaction.

To make ammonium nitrate, the factory uses ammonia and nitric acid:

$$NH_3 + HNO_3 \rightarrow NH_4NO_3$$

So each molecule of ammonia reacts with just one 'molecule' of acid to form one 'molecule' of ammonium nitrate. To find the relative mass of each 'molecule', you need to add together the relative atomic masses of all the atoms in the formula.

For ammonia, NH_3, the elements present are nitrogen and hydrogen. Look at the Periodic Table and check the **relative atomic masses** (N = 14, H = 1).

To find the **relative formula mass** of ammonia, add together the masses of all the atoms:

relative formula mass for NH_3 = 14 + 1 + 1 + 1 = 17

relative formula mass for HNO_3 = 1 + 14 + 16 + 16 + 16 = 63

relative formula mass for NH_4NO_3 = 14 + 1 + 1 + 1 + 1 + 14 + 16 + 16 + 16 = 80

We can use these numbers in the equation, provided that we keep the same units all the way through. Fertiliser factories work in tonnes, so:

$$NH_3 + HNO_3 \rightarrow NH_4NO_3$$

17 tonnes + 63 tonnes → 80 tonnes

So, to make 8000 tonnes of ammonium nitrate, we need:

- 8000 × 17/80 = 1700 tonnes of ammonia
- 8000 × 63/80 = 6300 tonnes of nitric acid.

Keeping the right soil pH

Acidity is measured using the pH scale (numbers below 7 are acid, numbers above 7 are alkaline). Most plants grow well only in a narrow range of pH.

Ammonium salts tend to make soil more acid (lower pH). Farmers spread lime (an alkali) on the land to stop it from becoming too acid.

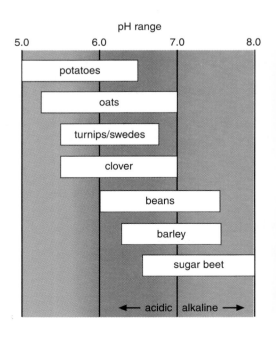

The pH range for best growth of crops.

Leaching of fertilisers

Plant roots can only absorb nutrients if the nutrients are in solution. Fertiliser must dissolve in water before it can do any good. If too much fertiliser is used, some will be washed out of the soil into local streams. The harmful effects of this are described in *Balancing acts*.

Which fertiliser gives the most nitrogen?

Ammonium sulphate and ammonium nitrate are both used as fertilisers. It is only the nitrogen in them that is useful to help plants grow. Which one of them provides most nitrogen?

- formula of ammonium sulphate is $(NH_4)_2SO_4$
- formula of ammonium nitrate is NH_4NO_3

Which elements are present in ammonium sulphate? Which elements are present in ammonium nitrate?

Both formulas contain two atoms of nitrogen, but which fertiliser contains the highest percentage of nitrogen?

The calculation for ammonium sulphate

The first step is to work out how many atoms of each element are present in the formula of the fertiliser.

In the formula of ammonium sulphate, there are two ammonium groups (NH_4), each of which contains a nitrogen atom and four hydrogen atoms. Altogether, $(NH_4)_2SO_4$ contains:

- 2 atoms of nitrogen
- 8 atoms of hydrogen
- 1 atom of sulphur
- 4 atoms of oxygen.

This table shows the stages in the calculation.

Element	No. of atoms	Relative atomic mass	Total mass of this element	Percentage by mass in the compound
nitrogen	2	14	28	$(28/132) \times 100 = 21.2\%$
hydrogen	8	1	8	$(8/132) \times 100 = 6.1\%$
sulphur	1	32	32	$(32/132) \times 100 = 24.2\%$
oxygen	4	16	64	$(64/132) \times 100 = 48.5\%$
Total			132	

? Things to do

1. Carry out the same steps to calculate the percentage by mass of each element in:

   a ammonium nitrate, NH_4NO_3 b ammonium phosphate $(NH_4)_2HPO_4$.

2. Arrange the three ammonium salts in order of which provides the most nitrogen for plant growth.

6 What we have we keep!

Other chemicals on the farm

Farmers can grow more than enough food to feed all of the world's population, but pests and diseases destroy much of the food before it can be eaten. The amount of food loss can be reduced by taking more care in farming, harvesting and storing food, and by using chemicals to combat pests and diseases.

Pesticides can be used to kill pests (for example, slugs or insects). **Herbicides** help to control weeds that might compete with the crop for light, space and nutrients.

The table shows how much of the food we grow is lost in different parts of the world.

Region of the world	Food lost (%)
Europe	25
Africa	42
Asia	43
Oceania	30
North America	29
South America	33

Using biological control

It is difficult to find chemicals for crop protection that affect just pests and leave other species unharmed. For example, pesticides might kill bees, which pollinate flowers, or ladybirds, which kill large numbers of the pest called greenfly.

One alternative is to use **biological control**, where one species is deliberately introduced to attack another species that is a pest. This article from a gardening magazine illustrates the idea.

A beetle with a taste for slugs

Scientists have discovered a beetle that likes eating slugs. It could be used as a harmless alternative to slug pellets, which can kill other useful creatures as well.

Slugs are covered with a slimy liquid, which contains chemicals that put off most other animals. Many beetles will approach a slug, touch it to investigate, then immediately back off and run away. The new beetle, which is called *Abax parallelepipedus*, does not: it decides that the slug is good food!

Trials have shown that the beetles, which grow up to one inch (2.5 cm) long, can control slugs in confined areas. Because the beetles are unable to fly, a small plastic barrier will ensure that they patrol only a given area.

Things to do

1.   a Make a bar chart to show the percentage loss of food in each region of the world.

   b Suggest why losses are higher in some regions.

   c Chemicals cost money. Explain how their use can lower the cost per tonne of producing food.

   d 'Organically grown' food is produced without using manufactured chemicals. Discuss why some people choose to buy organically grown foods even though they are more expensive.

Storing food safely

Many crops can only be harvested at certain times of the year. The food cannot all be eaten at once, and most of it must be stored so that supplies last through the year. Many things can happen to damage or destroy the food while it is in store.

Some foods can be processed to help them last longer; for example, peas or beans can be tinned, or they can be deep-frozen.

Many processing methods are very expensive, or rely on good transport and electricity supplies. Where these methods are not available, or are too expensive, stored food must be protected from pests. This can be done using pesticides, but other methods can also help.

Tall silos are often used to store harvested crops.

Storing maize in Togo

Maize is the most popular cereal grown in Togo, a country in West Africa. Farmers grow it both for their own food and to sell as a cash crop, which is often their only source of income.

The farmers can do several things to reduce the chance of damage to the stored maize.

- They harvest at exactly the right stage, as soon as the maize is ripened and begins to dry.
- After harvesting, they sort out and throw away any infested cobs.
- They raise the store off the ground to make it more difficult for rodents to climb in.
- They fill the air between the cobs with smoke to kill insects.
- They cover the granary to protect it against rain (but they must allow air to circulate, or the grain may rot).
- They use several small stores, not one big one, to reduce the chance of infestation spreading through the whole crop.

? Things to do

2 Read the article about the beetles that eat slugs and answer these questions.

a What methods do you know of to protect crops from being eaten by slugs?

b What are the disadvantages of using slug pellets?

c How do slugs protect themselves from being eaten by other animals?

d What makes the *Abax* beetle suitable for controlling slugs?

e What disadvantages might there be to using the beetles to control slugs?

3 Design a store to keep maize cobs. Explain the purpose of each part of your design.

Why does food spoil?

Our food comes from plants and animals. In all living tissue, many chemical reactions go on all the time. Many continue after the crop is harvested or the animal is dead. Some of these changes may cause food to spoil so that it becomes unsafe for eating.

When you cut up an apple and leave the pieces exposed to the air, the cut surface turns brown. Cutting the apple breaks cell walls and lets oxygen from the air react with the chemicals inside.

This food is covered in mould. It's no longer safe to eat.

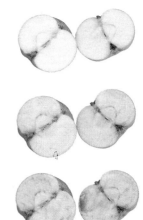

The way a slice of apple goes brown is just one example of food spoilage.

Enzymes: biological catalysts

Chemical reactions in living tissue are controlled by **enzymes**, which act as catalysts. Enzymes are very large protein molecules. (There is more about enzymes in *Keeping healthy*).

How enzymes work – a reminder

Each enzyme has an **active site** – a place on the surface where only one type of molecule (called the **substrate**) can fit and react.

This means enzymes are very **specific**. Each enzyme catalyses just one reaction. It also means they are very sensitive to changes in conditions that might alter the shape of the active site. If the active site changes shape, the substrate will no longer 'fit' and the reaction cannot happen.

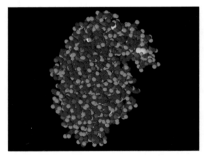

This is a model of a molecule of the enzyme pepsin.

Heating denatures enzymes

You can prevent pieces of apple from going brown by putting them in boiling water for about a minute. This is called 'blanching' (*blanche* is the French word for 'white'). The enzyme in the apple is heated well above its normal working temperature. Collisions with other molecules around the enzyme cause changes in the shape of its active site. We say the enzyme is **denatured**. The changes are permanent, and the enzyme can no longer work, even after it has cooled down.

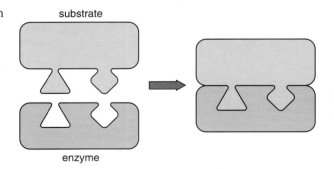

Enzymes are usually very specific – they only work with one kind of substrate molecule.

Why pickling preserves food

Enzymes are also very sensitive to changes in acidity. They only work within a very narrow range of pH. For example, you can keep apple pieces white by squeezing lemon juice (an acid) over them.

Pickling preserves food by keeping it in vinegar, a solution of a weak acid called **ethanoic acid**. The acid stops the action of enzymes that cause spoilage reactions.

Using enzymes – apple juice (SS) FT13

The acid in vinegar stops the onions from 'going off'.

Enzymes can be extracted from cells and used in many ways. For example, the enzyme papain is used in toothpaste to break down food residues on your teeth.

One large-scale use of an enzyme is in extracting juice from apples. Apple juice is squeezed from crushed apples. Apples contain a substance called pectin, which thickens the juice and makes it difficult to extract. If the enzyme pectinase is added, it breaks down the pectin. The juice can be extracted more easily and is less cloudy.

Using enzymes – soft-centred chocolates (SS) FT14

Many soft-centred chocolates contain fondant, a mixture of tiny sugar crystals and water. The fondant must be hard enough to keep its shape as it is coated with chocolate. If the enzyme invertase is added to the fondant, it slowly breaks down the sugar (sucrose) into simpler sugars and water. The simpler sugars partly dissolve, making the centre much softer and runnier – *after* it has been sealed inside the chocolate coating.

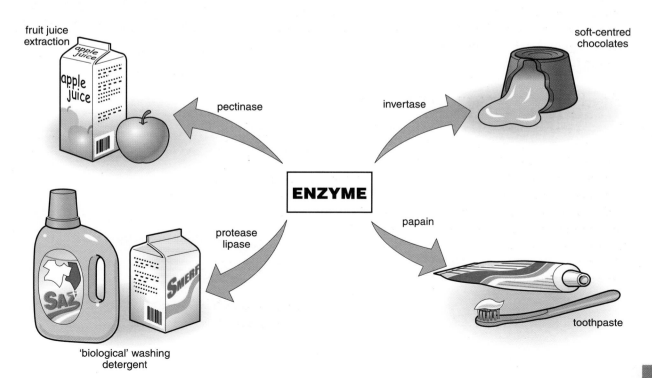

Enzymes have many uses in the manufacture of useful products.

Fermentation (SS) FT15

Yeasts are single-celled fungi. They are small enough to be carried on the wind. When they settle on fruits, they feed on the sugars within the fruit cells. If plenty of air is available, sugar is broken down completely to release energy, forming carbon dioxide and water.

If air is kept out, enzymes from the yeast can only partly break down the sugar, to form carbon dioxide and alcohol. This reaction is called **fermentation**. For thousands of years, yeast has been used to ferment fruit sugar in making wine.

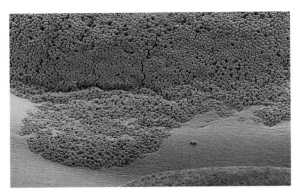

Yeasts are single-celled fungi.

Making wine

Many people use yeast to make their own wine or beer. Yeast is mixed with fruit juice to make wine, or with barley, water and hops to make beer. The yeast feeds on sugar in the solution, fermenting it and releasing carbon dioxide and alcohol (ethanol). The word equation for fermentation is:

> glucose → carbon dioxide + ethanol

Fermentation only happens when air is kept out. It is an example of **anaerobic respiration**. (More details about this are given in the year 11 unit *Staying alive*).

The kit includes these instructions:

To ensure success
- use an air-lock
- keep at 25–30 °C
- wash all equipment with sodium metabisulphite solution before use.

Bread-making: another use for yeast

The dough used for making bread contains flour, water, sugar and yeast. The yeast feeds on the sugar, making bubbles of carbon dioxide gas. These bubbles are trapped in the dough, and make it swell or 'rise'. When the dough is baked, these bubbles give a lighter, stiffer texture to the bread. Alcohol is also produced, but bread does not make you drunk, because the alcohol evaporates away during cooking!

Bread rises because of the carbon dioxide gas given off as the yeast ferments the sugar in the dough.

Investigating bread dough

Jack mixed flour, yeast and water to form a dough. He divided the dough into six equal-sized pieces. He put one piece into a measuring cylinder and recorded its volume. He took the other pieces and mixed each one with a different sugar. Then he put each of these in a measuring cylinder. He left the six cylinders in a water-bath at 30 °C for an hour. Jack then recorded the volume of dough in each cylinder.

Treatment	Starting vol (cm³)	Final vol (cm³)	Change in vol (cm³)
no sugar	30	30	0
added glucose	30	45	
added sucrose	30	39	
added fructose	30	42	
added lactose	30	32	
added maltose	30	35	

Wine into vinegar

Do you put vinegar on your food? Vinegar is a dilute solution of ethanoic acid. The name may give you a clue where it comes from. 'Vinegar' (from *vin*, the French word for 'wine') is made by a second fermentation of wine, using a bacterium *Acetobacter* in the presence of air. It is the same process that causes wine to turn sour and vinegary if left exposed to the air for too long. The ethanol (alcohol) is oxidised to ethanoic acid, a weak acid:

ethanol + oxygen → ethanoic acid

Vinegar is used for flavouring food and also for preserving it. Pickles are made using vinegar. The weak acid is enough to stop enzymes in the food from causing changes that would spoil it, and to stop bacteria from growing.

If you test vinegar and dilute hydrochloric acid with Universal Indicator, you will notice that vinegar gives a reading of about pH4. This is acidic, but much less acidic than hydrochloric acid (about pH1).

Other ways of preserving foods

Many methods of preserving food have been invented and some of these involve adding chemicals to the food to prevent spoilage reactions. Only certain permitted substances may be added to foods for commercial sale. These food additives are given code numbers (called E-numbers) to identify them. Look on packages of food at home to find examples.

Things to do

1 Look at the instructions on the home brew label opposite, and answer the following questions.

  a Why do you think the equipment has to be washed through with sodium metabisulphite before the contents are added?

  b Why is the air-lock needed?

  c Why do you think the container should be kept at about 25–30 °C?

  d Explain why lots of bubbles can be seen during fermentation. What gas is in the bubbles?

2 a Look at the table on this page. Copy it out, and fill in the last column.

  b What is the purpose of the tube with no sugar?

  c Use your knowledge about how enzymes work to explain the results with the different sugars.

Questions 1–5 are about these chemicals:

A	ammonium phosphate	$(NH_4)_2HPO_4$
B	ammonium nitrate	NH_4NO_3
C	nitric acid	HNO_3
D	nitrogen	N_2
E	potassium chloride	KCl

Choose from these chemicals, the one which –

1 Is a gas at room temperature and pressure.

2 Is reacted with ammonia to make a fertiliser.

3 Does **not** contain nitrogen.

4 Contains more than one element which is important for plant growth.

5 Is made up of the greatest number of different elements.

6 Ammonia reacts with acids to form salts, for example –

Ammonium nitrate
Ammonium phosphate
Ammonium sulphate

a Name the acids needed to form each of these salts.

b Write word equations for the reactions by which the salts are formed.

c Write balanced chemical equations for these reactions.

7 Which of the following substances are formed by plants from nitrates in the soil?

A	Ammonia	B	Starch
C	Carbohydrates	D	Proteins
E	Fats		

8 Describe how you could test a sample of gas to see whether it contained ammonia.

9 What is the percentage by weight of nitrogen in ammonia gas?

10 In the Haber process, ammonia is made by reaction between nitrogen and hydrogen.

a Write a balanced equation for this reaction.

b Explain why the reaction is carried out under high pressure.

c Explain why the gases have to be heated to make the reaction commercially possible.

d Explain why it is important to keep the temperature as low as possible.

e What is used as a catalyst in this reaction?

Only part of the nitrogen and hydrogen is turned into ammonia

f How is the ammonia separated from unreacted nitrogen and hydrogen?

g What is done with the unreacted nitrogen and hydrogen? Explain how this makes the process more profitable.

11 Describe the main stages in the manufacture of sulphuric acid from sulphur by the contact process.

Questions 12 and 13 are about these types of additives which may be put into foods:

A	Colours	B	Preservatives
C	Emulsifiers	D	Flavours
E	Anti-oxidants		

12 Which of these slows down the growth of microbes in food?

13 Which is added to improve the look of the food?

14 Fertilisers cost money.

How can using fertilisers help a farmer to produce crops at a lower cost per tonne?

Suggest two disadvantages of using very large amounts of fertiliser.

15 Some ways of preserving food depend on changing conditions so that enzymes which cause food to spoil cannot work. Explain how each of these methods changes the conditions in the food:

a Pickling onions in vinegar

b Turning fruit into jam

c Drying fruit

INTRODUCING
Restless Earth

...any different processes affect the Earth and its atmosphere.

Try these first

1 What is the percentage of:

   a nitrogen in air   b oxygen in air?

2 What other gases are present in air?

3 There are three types of rock:

   igneous   sedimentary   metamorphic

   Which type of rock:

   a is formed from molten magma

   b is made of deposited grains

   c is formed from other rocks under high pressure and/or temperature

   d is formed in volcanoes

   e crystalises from molten rock

   f is formed by recrystalisation in the solid state

   g contains fossils?

4 Sea cliffs are eroded when the sea breaks off pieces of rock and moves them away with the tide. List some other ways rocks can be eroded.

In this unit you will learn:

- about the structure of the Earth and how we find out about it
- how the oceans and atmosphere were formed
- how the Earth keeps warm
- how enormous plates on the Earth's surface are involved in forming and destroying rock
- about earthquakes and volcanoes
- about clues to the past, buried in the rocks.

Energy for the Solar System

The Solar System.

The **Sun** is our nearest star. It **radiates** energy in all directions into the space around it. Some of this radiation is **absorbed** by the **planets** that make up the **Solar System** and it warms them up. It is possible to predict the surface temperature of each planet by thinking about how far away each one is from the Sun – can you predict a pattern for these temperatures?

How hot are the planets?

The actual surface temperatures of the planets do not fit the simple predicted pattern.

Planet	Distance from Sun ($\times 10^6$ km)	Surface temperature (°C)		Atmosphere
		Predicted	**Actual**	
Mercury	60	167	167	hardly any atmosphere
Venus	110	7	467	very dense atmosphere
Earth	150	−33	17	dense atmosphere
Moon	150	−33	−33	no atmosphere
Mars	230	−68	−63	very little atmosphere
Jupiter	780	−183	−103	very dense atmosphere

It can be cold in space!

? Things to do

1   Draw a graph of the predicted temperature of each planet against its distance from the Sun. Now mark on the graph the actual surface temperature of each planet. Which ones are different from the predicted temperatures? Can you explain this difference?

2   Imagine you took a flask of drinking water on a space voyage.

   a On which planets would it turn to ice?   **b** On which planets would it turn to steam?

3   Draw some joke cartoons to show how hot or cold a space traveller would feel on Mercury and on Jupiter.

Radiation to and from space

The Sun is very hot and gives out high energy, short wavelength radiation. This solar radiation is mainly UV (ultraviolet) and visible light. This heats up the Earth. Some of the energy is radiated back from the surface of the Earth.

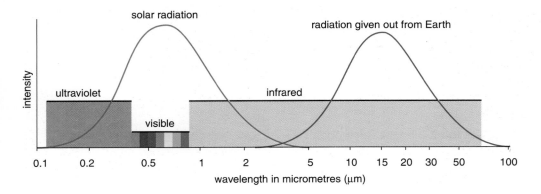

This electromagnetic spectrum shows the radiation given off by the Sun and by the Earth.

The Earth is much cooler than the Sun and so gives out lower energy, longer wavelength radiation. This is mainly IR (infrared) radiation.

The global 'greenhouse'

Gases in the Earth's atmosphere let the high energy radiation from the Sun pass through. The radiation warms up the Earth. However, some gases, such as **carbon dioxide**, absorb the lower energy radiation given off by the Earth. This energy cannot escape, so the Earth gets warmer. A greenhouse acts in the same way – the Sun's rays come through the glass, but the heat rays from the warm soil and plants cannot escape. Our atmosphere acts like a giant greenhouse. Gases that trap heat are called 'greenhouse gases'.

Who is right? Discuss this with your group.

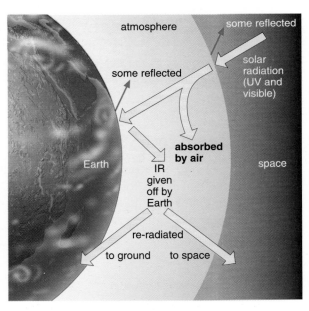

The 'greenhouse effect'.

Where did our atmosphere come from?

About 4000 million years ago, our Earth was a ball of very hot rock, with a very thin crust. Molten rock erupted through many volcanoes that covered the land. Gases bubbled out of molten rock to make an early atmosphere for Earth.

The table shows information about the gases that come from an active volcano in Hawaii. Scientists think our early atmosphere came from similar volcanoes and so contained similar gases.

The Earth looked very different 4000 million years ago.

Gas	Volcanic gases (Earth's early atmosphere) (%)	Earth's atmosphere today (%)
nitrogen	5	78
oxygen	0	21
carbon dioxide	12	0.03
water vapour	74	less than 1
sulphur dioxide	9	trace (almost 0)

Things to do

1. Draw a comparison bar chart to show the amounts of each gas in our atmosphere 4000 million years ago compared to today (use a spreadsheet or graph paper).

2. Which gases have increased in amount? Which have decreased?

3. What happened to the water vapour as the temperature of the Earth cooled? Why is this vitally important to the evolution of life?

Oxygen for life RE6

The first simple living organisms appeared 3500 million years ago. These tiny living things can be seen as fossils in very old rocks. At first, living things only existed several metres under water where the water protected them from strong ultraviolet radiation from the Sun.

About 3000 million years ago, some of these microscopic organisms began to use energy from sunlight to make carbohydrate (glucose) from carbon dioxide and water. This is photosynthesis, and these minute living things were the first plants.

$$6H_2O + 6CO_2 \xrightarrow[\text{energy from sunlight}]{} C_6H_{12}O_6 + 6O_2$$

water + carbon dioxide $\xrightarrow{\hspace{2cm}}$ glucose + oxygen

Oxygen began to build up in the atmosphere. At first, this happened very slowly because metal compounds in rocks reacted with the oxygen and removed it. For example, green iron(II) compounds reacted with oxygen to make brown iron(III) compounds. A similar thing happens today when iron reacts with oxygen to make rust, an iron(III) compound. Iron(II) compounds are common in rocks that were formed *before* there was very much oxygen in the atmosphere.

When oxygen began to build up in the atmosphere, some of it reacted to make **ozone**. This formed a layer high in the atmosphere, which screens the surface of the Earth from the Sun's ultraviolet rays.

The carbon dioxide story

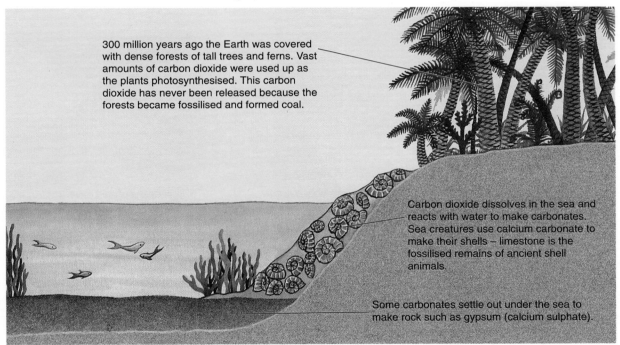

300 million years ago the Earth was covered with dense forests of tall trees and ferns. Vast amounts of carbon dioxide were used up as the plants photosynthesised. This carbon dioxide has never been released because the forests became fossilised and formed coal.

Carbon dioxide dissolves in the sea and reacts with water to make carbonates. Sea creatures use calcium carbonate to make their shells – limestone is the fossilised remains of ancient shell animals.

Some carbonates settle out under the sea to make rock such as gypsum (calcium sulphate).

Carbon dioxide is 'locked up' in fossil fuels, and also in rock sediments.

Things to do

4   Discuss why animals could not exist on Earth without photosynthesis.

5   Look at the table opposite. Volcanic gases contain only a little nitrogen. Explain why the percentage of nitrogen in air has become so large.

6   Over the last 100 years, humans have been burning coal in very large quantities. Why do we burn so much coal? Describe what you think the Earth will be like if all the carbon dioxide 'locked up' in fossil fuels is released.

3 Salts in the seas

Where did our oceans come from?

The early Earth was covered in active volcanoes, and more than 70% of the gases from the magma (molten rock) was water vapour. For millions of years the Earth was so hot that the water stayed as a gas, but as the Earth cooled, it eventually condensed to form seas of distilled water.

The Vikings believed that an enormous, evil ice-giant, called Ymir, melted and his melt-w made the seas.

Why is the sea salty?

The first land was made of igneous rock from cooled, solidified magma. The rocks were full of salts containing many different elements that had come from the Earth's mantle, deep underground. After the seas were formed, the heat from the Sun evaporated the water from the seas, which began the 'water cycle'. The water vapour condensed to make rain, and ran over the land, weathering the rocks, and dissolving salts.
The salts were then carried into the sea.

water vapour cools and condenses

rainwater

water vapour

heat energy from the sun evaporates water from the sea

rainwater runs over the rocks into the sea, causing **erosion**

seawater

Over millions of years, the water cycle gradually carries more and more dissolved salts into the sea.

The most soluble salts, such as sodium chloride, dissolved most easily in the rainwater. Even today, river water contains sodium, potassium and calcium salts that dissolve out of the surrounding rocks.

Things to do

1   **Chemical weathering** happens when compounds in the rocks dissolve in rainwater. Here are the names of some other processes that happen when water flows over rocks. Find out what these words mean.

    erosion   deposition

2   Find some igneous rocks or pebbles, or igneous rock in local buildings. Look carefully for crystals.

Chemistry in the sea

When salts dissolve in water, they separate into ions. All salts have a metal cation (positive ion) and a non-metal anion (negative ion). For example, when solid sodium chloride dissolves in water it separates into sodium and chloride ions:

$$NaCl\ (s) \rightarrow Na^+\ (aq) + Cl^-\ (aq)$$

The sea contains many different ions. Some have been washed from the land, some come from volcanic activity under the sea and some come from gases in the air dissolving in the seawater. In some countries, the seawater is collected and evaporated in enormous salt pans. The salts form crystals and are sold to be used as raw materials in the chemical industry.

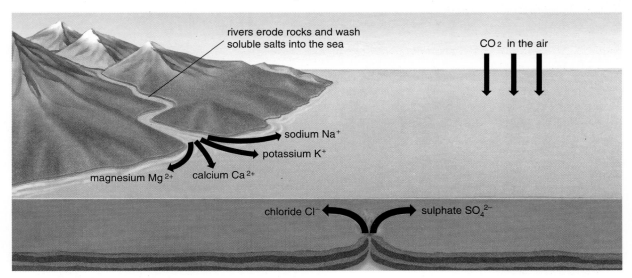

rivers erode rocks and wash soluble salts into the sea

CO_2 in the air

sodium Na^+
potassium K^+
magnesium Mg^{2+} calcium Ca^{2+}
chloride Cl^- sulphate SO_4^{2-}

Many different ions get into the sea, in many different ways.

Shellfish absorb calcium ions and carbonate ions from sea water to form calcium carbonate shells.

$$Ca^{2+}\ (aq) + CO_3^{2-}\ (aq) \rightarrow CaCO_3\ (s)$$

Most chalk and limestone is formed from fossil remains of shells.

As land-locked seas or lakes evaporate, they become more concentrated. Ions begin to join together to form fine particles of solid which are precipitated as sediments. Deposits such as gypsum (calcium sulphate) or rock salt are formed in this way.

Ammonite from chalk and limestone rocks.

Things to do

3   Find out what sodium, chlorine, calcium and magnesium compounds are used for.

4   Discuss why sodium and chloride ions have been able to reach quite high concentrations in the sea, while many other elements have been removed as sediments.

4 Journey into the Earth

An imaginary journey

Over a century ago, Jules Verne wrote an adventure book, *Journey to the Centre of the Earth*, about a group of travellers who tunnelled through the Earth in a machine. They met amazing, enormous animals.

To reach the centre of the Earth, we would have to make a tunnel nearly 6400 km deep. We would have to travel through rock at thousands of degrees centigrade. Today, our deepest hole is a drill shaft in Russia, which reaches 12 km into the Earth – less than $\frac{1}{500}$ of the radius of the Earth. How do we know about the centre of the Earth when nobody has been there?

Seismic waves

Earthquakes send out shock waves. By studying where the shock waves can be felt, and where they cannot, geologists have built up a picture of the inside of the Earth. The shock waves sent out by earthquakes are called seismic waves. There are three types.

Type of wave	Direction of vibration	Speed	Movement of rock
P wave	longitudinal – they pull and push the rocks in the direction of travel	fast through solids; slower through liquids	
S wave	transverse – force the rocks to move side to side	slow through solids; cannot travel through liquids	
L wave	they 'ripple' the surface of the Earth moving it up and down causing the most damage	slow; only affect the surface	

Recording earthquake waves

Stations are set up all over the world to record seismic waves using instruments called seismometers.

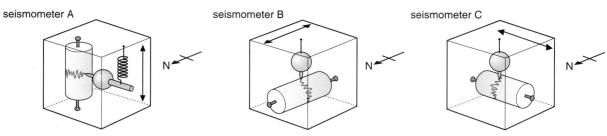

Each seismometer records the seismic vibrations in a different direction.

What do earthquake waves show about the structure of the Earth?

The waves travel at different speeds through rocks with different **densities.** Analysing the speed of the earthquake waves picked up by seismometers around the world suggests that the Earth has four layers. The outer layer – the **crust**, which carries the continents and oceans – is very thin and not very dense. The **mantle** is much more dense and is made of solid rock. It 'rings like a bell' after an earthquake. The mantle can flow very slowly.

After an earthquake, some seismometers around the Earth do not record S-waves. S-waves cannot travel through liquid, so there must be a layer of liquid rock inside the Earth. This is the **outer core**.

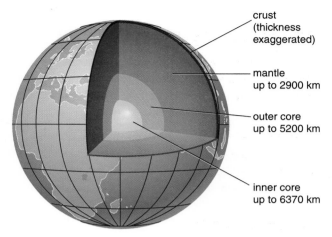

crust
(thickness
exaggerated)

mantle
up to 2900 km

outer core
up to 5200 km

inner core
up to 6370 km

The Earth has a solid inner core, a liquid outer core, a solid mantle and a thin, solid crust.

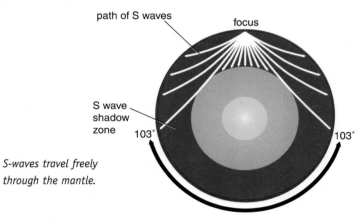

path of S waves

focus

S wave shadow zone   103°

103°

S-waves travel freely through the mantle.

Things to do

1   Look at the pictures of the seismometers. Which seismometers record the Earth shaking side to side? Which ones record up and down movement? Which seismometer will detect L waves?

2   Draw 'circles in boxes' diagrams to show how the particles are arranged in the liquid outer core and the solid inner core. Use your diagrams to explain why the inner core is very dense.

3   Look at these two recordings of waves from the same earthquake:

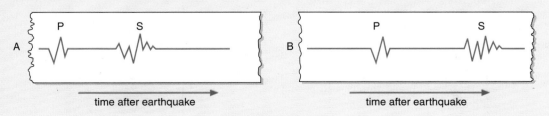

a Why do the P waves arrive before the S waves?

b Which recording, **A** or **B**, was made furthest away from the earthquake? Explain your answer.

5 The Earth moves

Ideas about the surface of the Earth

In 1915, Alfred Wegener published a book explaining his theory that the continents are constantly moving. He thought of this idea when he watched giant sheets of ice moving around on the Arctic sea.

Wegener had heard suggestions that the continents must once have been joined together. In some places the layers of rock types match very closely across different continents. Many similar fossils – such as the tree fern, *Glossopteris* – are found in Africa, America, India and Australia. These **observations** could not be explained, because the continents were so far apart. Wegener suggested that the continents were solid masses that 'drifted' across the Earth's surface and so had moved apart over millions of years. Since then, studies of earthquakes and volcanoes have modified the theory.

Tree fern fossils are the remains of warm, tropical forests.

? Things to do

1   Look at the layers of rock found on the coasts of Africa and South America.

   a What evidence suggests that the continents were once joined together?

   b Geologists believe that the continents split apart 120 million years ago. What evidence shows that they may be right?

2   Some people believe that rock formations like this show evidence of a great flood. They believe that many living things died because they did not get onto Noah's Ark.

   a What evidence supports this idea?

   b What evidence does not fit this idea?

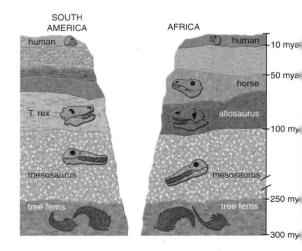

The rock profiles at the coasts of South America and Africa are remarkably similar, which suggests that they were once joined.

Land on a plate

Wegener's theory of 'continental drift' was unable to explain how the continents could move. This can now be explained because we have a much better understanding of the structure of the Earth.

In terms of chemical structure, the Earth has an outer **crust**, rich in silicon-containing rocks, and with fewer iron-containing rocks. This crust is less dense than the **mantle** below, which contains a higher proportion of iron-rich rocks. Below the mantle is the **core**. The outer part of the core is liquid, the inner core is solid.

Mechanical boundaries between layers come at slightly different depths. The outermost layer of the mantle is solid. Together with the crust, it makes up the **lithosphere**. The lithosphere is divided up into large plates, called **tectonic plates**. It is these plates that move, carrying continents with them.

These huge plates can move because the part of the mantle below them (called the **asthenosphere**) is very hot. Although it is still solid, it is near its melting point and can flow very slowly, carrying the plates with it. (Solids can 'flow' and change shape like this – think what happens to modelling clay if you apply a force, or the very slow movement of ice in a glacier.)

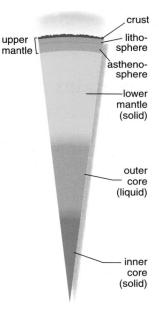

We now know much more detail about the structure of the Earth.

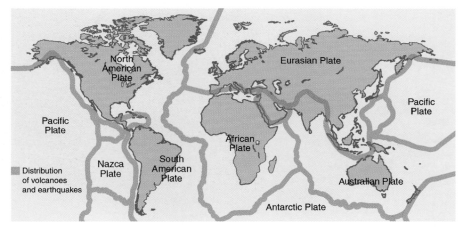

The 'hot spots' for earthquakes and volcanoes coincide with the edges of the tectonic plates.

Problems at the edges of plates

The movement of tectonic plates causes huge forces where the plates meet. Look at the map above of where volcanoes are found and earthquakes happen. The danger areas show where the edges of the plates meet.

When plates slip and move, the energy released causes earthquakes, which can do enormous damage.

Things to do

3   Explain why earthquakes rarely happen in Britain.

6 Plates moving apart

Mountains beneath the sea

In 1870, a research ship called *HMS Challenger* began to make maps of the floor of the Atlantic Ocean. The crew were amazed to find enormous mountains and volcanoes, which formed a huge ridge down the middle of the ocean, now known as the Mid-Atlantic Ridge. These mountains were mapped in detail by submarines of the US Navy in the 1940s.

The researchers who mapped the ocean floors were astounded by what they found.

Plates moving apart

The plates that carry North and South America are slowly moving away from the one that carries Africa. The lower pressure on the mantle below means that some of it melts and molten magma forces its way up between the plates. The magma cools, solidifies, and forms new rocks as the plates are moved apart. This is called **ocean floor spreading**.

The new rocks form a ridge in the ocean floor (called an **oceanic ridge**).

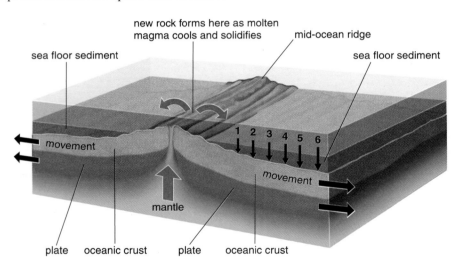

New ocean floor is created as magma spills up between the plates and cools.

Things to do

1 If two plates are moving apart at a rate of 10 cm a year, how much wider will the ocean between them be after 1000 years?

2 How does the discovery of the Mid-Atlantic Ridge support the theory of plate tectonics?

3 Samples of rock from the Mid-Atlantic Ridge have been analysed. Discuss with your group which of the following statements is true about the rocks from the ridge.

  a The rocks contain crystals.   b The rocks contain the same elements as molten magma.

  c The rocks contain fossils.   d The rocks are older than the surrounding rocks.

  e The rocks are igneous.   f The rocks are formed in layers.

How do we know that the sea floor is spreading?

In the 1960s, a research ship took samples of sedimentary rock from the sea floor at increasing distances from the Mid-Atlantic Ridge. These were then tested to find out their ages. This is a table of the results.

* See the numbers in the table opposite to show where the samples were taken from.

Point where sample was taken*	Distance from the ridge (km)	Age of oldest rock (million years)
1	100	5
2	300	15
3	700	35
4	1000	50
5	1300	65
6	1600	80

Evidence from magnetism

The crew on the ships that were mapping the Atlantic sea floor discovered that compasses pointed in the wrong direction when they were held close to some areas of rocks. They called these areas **magnetic stripes**.

Magnetic stripes have also been found either side of other mid-ocean ridges. They occur because the north and south poles of the Earth's magnetic field have reversed at times during the Earth's history. Iron particles, trapped in the rock as it solidifies, are magnetised in the same direction as the Earth's magnetic field *at that time*. This discovery supports the theory about how ocean floor spreading occurs by the continual formation of new rock at the gap between the plates.

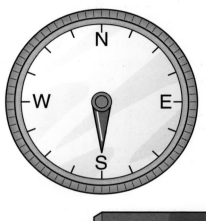

A magnet can cause a compass to point the wrong way.

Things to do

4   a Look at the table above. Draw a graph of age of rock against distance from the ridge.

b How does your graph show that the sea floor is spreading at a constant rate.

5   Look at the diagram opposite, explaining ocean floor spreading. Why are the layers of sea floor sediment very thin near the ridge, and thicker further away?

6   Look at this diagram of magnetic stripes.

a Which area of rock is exactly the same age as rock area X?

b Which rock areas are the oldest?

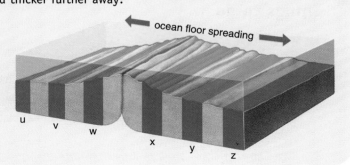

Rocks going down

New rock is being made all the time at ocean ridges. However, the Earth's surface does not get any bigger. How is rock removed from the crust? Where two plates move towards one another, one sinks and the rock is melted or taken into the mantle. This is called **subduction**.

The rock cycle

Rocks are continually formed and taken away from the crust by the movement of tectonic plates. This forms a huge recycling process.

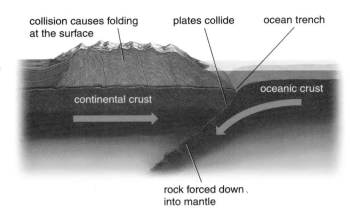

collision causes folding at the surface
plates collide
ocean trench
continental crust
oceanic crust
rock forced down into mantle

Rock from the Earth's crust is pushed back down into the mantle when two plates collide.

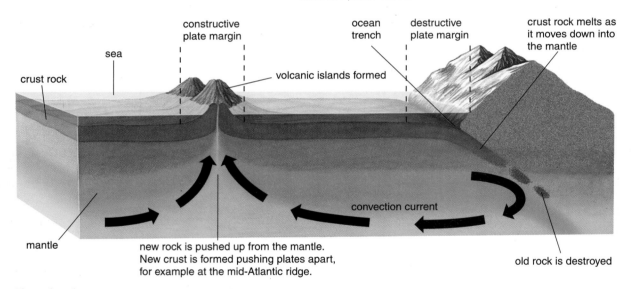

constructive plate margin
sea
crust rock
ocean trench
destructive plate margin
crust rock melts as it moves down into the mantle
volcanic islands formed
convection current
mantle
new rock is pushed up from the mantle. New crust is formed pushing plates apart, for example at the mid-Atlantic ridge.
old rock is destroyed

The rock cycle.

? Things to do

1. Subduction only happens where two plates moving towards each other are of different density. Explain why the difference in density is important.

2. a High mountain ranges are often found along the coasts of continents. The Rockies in Canada are an example. Use ideas about subduction to explain how they were formed.

   b Use an atlas to find other mountain ranges near plate boundaries, which may have been formed in the same way.

3. Write about the life story of a piece of rock from when it is formed at a mid-ocean ridge to when it sinks back down into the mantle. Include as many of the following words as you can:

   magma   **melted**   **solidified**   **igneous**   **erosion**   **weathering**

   transported   **deposited**   **sedimentary**   **metamorphic**   **subduction**   **recycle**

Volcanoes

Where two plates move towards each other, the huge pressure often folds the rocks, pushing them up to form mountains. The subducting plate partly melts and magma may rise, forming volcanoes. This is why volcanoes are found along the lines where plates meet. Volcanoes at subduction zones are often very explosive and dangerous.

The build-up of pressure forces volcanic gases to shoot out of the volcano.

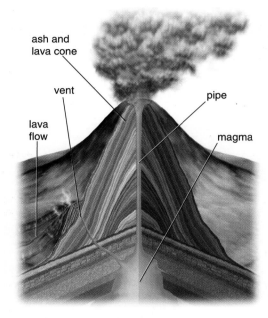

Volcanoes occur where magma is forced up to the surface.

Fold mountains

Fold mountains are often formed when two continental plates push together. Mount Everest and the Himalayas formed when the plate carrying India collided with the plate carrying Asia. The rocks on top of the plates became folded and were pushed up.

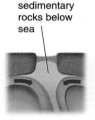

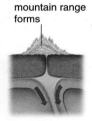

1 plates move towards each other

2 plates move closer together

3 plates collide

Sedimentary rock formed at the seabed is squeezed up as the plates collide, to form mountains.

?

Things to do

4   Volcanic gases contain large amounts of sulphur dioxide, carbon dioxide and hydrogen sulphide. Use school Hazard cards to find out why these gases can be dangerous to people.

5   In 1998, the volcano in the middle of the island of Monserrat erupted.

  a Describe the dangers to people living nearby when a volcano erupts.

  The volcano caused huge clouds of volcanic ash to cover the island.

  b How might this affect the lives of local people?

6   If a plate carrying oceanic crust pushes against a continental plate, the oceanic plate sinks underneath, pushing up rock sediments where the plates meet.

  a Use this idea to explain why fossils of sea shells are found on the tops of mountains in the Pyrenees (you can find the Pyrenees in an atlas).

8 History in the rocks

Looking at rocks

Sedimentary rock is formed from particles settling to the bottom of the sea, a swamp or a valley to form layers. As more and more layers of sediment build up, the particles are squashed and cemented together to form rock. Sedimentary rock is usually formed in layers, is not made up of crystals and often contains fossils of organisms that lived in the water as the rock was being formed.

We can look at sedimentary rock for clues to tell us about what the area was like when the rock was formed. There may be clues to tell us about past climates and whether the land was covered by forests, seas or fresh water.

Corals live in clear water in warm tropical seas.

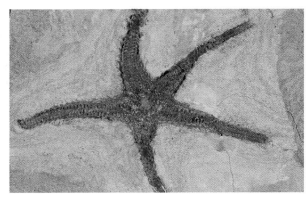

Starfish and mussels live in cool seas, in a climate similar to Britain today.

Ripples in sandstone show that it was formed from a beach near a shallow sea.

Restless Earth

How old are the rocks?

The age of one rock layer compared to another layer is judged by working out which one was formed first. A lower rock layer is usually older than a rock layer above it.

This only tells us how old the rocks are *compared* to each other. To find the *real age* of rocks, geologists use radioactivity. (You will find out about radioactivity in year 11, in *Seeing inside the body*.)

Some elements in rocks break down; for example, uranium slowly breaks down to form lead. The **half-life** for the reaction is the time it takes for half the element to break down – about 700 million years in the case of uranium. Geologists can tell how old a rock is by comparing the amount of uranium left with the amount of different isotopes of lead.

If sedimentary rocks containing fossils can be dated, then the age of the fossils is also known. Fossils of the same type can be used to date rocks in other places.

The history of the Earth

The timeline shows what we know about the history of the Earth. The timeline would be five times the length of this page, but the period before 600 million years ago has been left out. It is very difficult to grasp how long the Earth has existed.

If we scale down the life of the Earth so that the Earth is just one day old, then the dinosaurs died out two hours ago having lived for about three hours. We humans have only just been born, a second before midnight!

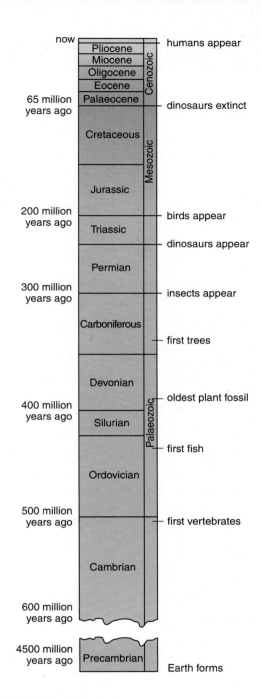

A brief history of the Earth.

Things to do

1 Draw a bar chart to show how long each type of life-form has been on Earth.

2 What types of fossils might be found in rock that is:

a 150 million years old   b 350 million years old   c 500 million years old?

1   This graph shows how gases in the atmosphere have changed since the Earth was formed.

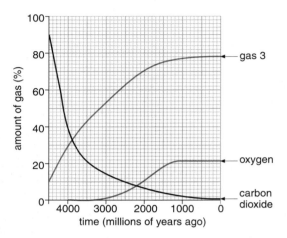

a The first plants appeared on Earth 3000 million years ago. What happened to the amount of oxygen in the atmosphere after the plants appeared? Why did this change happen?

b When animals appeared, they began using up the oxygen. Use the graph to predict when animals appeared on Earth.

c The amount of carbon dioxide has fallen to a tiny amount in today's atmosphere. List all the processes that remove carbon dioxide from the atmosphere.

d How much of gas 3 is in the atmosphere today? Name gas 3.

2   Which of the rocks below are igneous, sedimentary and metamorphic? Give reasons for your decisions.

3   Look at this diagram of the rock cycle.

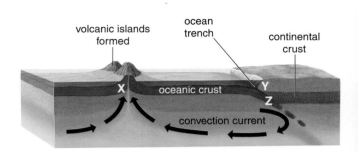

a Explain why this is called the 'rock cycle'.

b How many plates are shown on this diagram?

c What type of rocks will form in the areas labelled X, Y and Z?

d Why does the oceanic plate move under the continental plate?

e What happens to the rock in the oceanic plate as it sinks into the mantle?

f Explain how the volcanic island was formed.

4   Earthquakes and volcanoes often happen in the area where two plates meet. Use books, CD-ROMs or the Internet to find out about one area where either earthquakes or volcanoes happen. What do people living in such a place do to try to lessen the danger and damage?

5   Find Mount Everest on a world map. Then explain how it is possible for it to be made of limestone.

Electricity in the home

Try these first

Draw the circuit diagram for two lamps in series with a 3 V battery. Include an ammeter to measure the current in the lamps.

Draw the circuit diagram for two lamps in parallel with a 3 V battery. Include a voltmeter to measure the voltage of the battery.

Copy this diagram of a simple circuit:

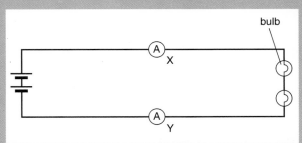

The current at point X is 2 amp.

a What is the current in amperes at point Y?

b How would the current change if you added an extra bulb?

c How would the current change if you added an extra cell to the battery?

d If one bulb broke, what would happen to the other one?

Look at the circuit above. What is being transferred from the battery of cells to the lamp? Choose from this list.

current   energy   force   light

Electricity can have some hair-raising effects!

In this unit you will learn:

- about the structure of atoms
- how insulators become charged by the transfer of electrons
- the uses and hazards of static electricity
- how a current of electrons in a conductor transfers electrical energy
- about the effects of changing resistance in a circuit
- how to calculate the electrical energy transferred
- how to calculate the resistance of a circuit
- how to connect things safely to the mains electricity supply
- about the different ways of heating using electricity.

1 What is electricity?

Using electricity

You use electricity every day. For example, electrical energy can be transferred for:

- heating food quickly in a microwave oven
- reproducing music through a radio receiver
- sending an e-mail to a friend.

All of these things are only possible because of electricity. But what is electricity?

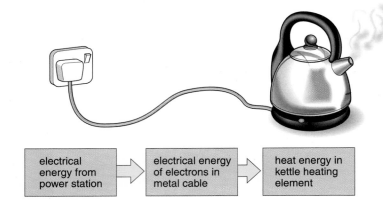

| electrical energy from power station | → | electrical energy of electrons in metal cable | → | heat energy in kettle heating element |

This energy transfer diagram shows how electricity heats up water in a kettle.

Electricity is the transfer of energy from one place to another by the motion of tiny charged particles.

Conductors and insulators

Some substances allow electricity to pass through them easily. They are called **conductors**. Metals are good conductors, so the wires in electrical circuits are made of metal.

Some other materials offer great resistance to electricity. They are called **insulators**. Many plastics are good insulators, so electrical wiring is often covered with plastic to protect the user.

Charging up

Friction – caused by rubbing things together – often transfers electric charge from one substance to another. If the substances are insulators, the charge builds up. This is **static electricity** – electricity stuck in one place!

Have you ever walked across a carpet, then got a slight electric shock when you touched a metal door handle? Friction with the carpet builds up a charge on you, which is quickly discharged when you touch the door handle (a conductor). If the discharge is sudden, static electricity can cause sparks, as the charge 'jumps' to the conductor. If you wear an acrylic jumper over a nylon shirt, and undress in the dark, you will see sparks as static electricity discharges!

Making sparks

Hand-held gas lighters make sparks on purpose, to light the gas in a cooker or boiler. They contain a special material known as a **piezocrystal**.

When the crystal is squeezed hard, some **electrons** are displaced in the crystal. Electrons are the tiny particles that carry electric charge in metals. They move away from the crystal along the copper wire. As the electrons jump across the gap, they transfer their electrical energy into heat (which lights the gas), a flash of light, and a crackling noise!

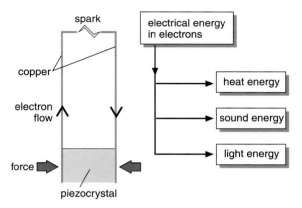

Piezocrystals are used in gas lighters to make sparks.

Charge

When a piezocrystal is squeezed, its ends become **charged**. This is because electrons have a property known as **negative charge**. So as the electrons build up at one end of the piezocrystal, that end becomes **negatively charged**. At the same time, the other end – which is now lacking electrons – becomes **positively charged**.

Atoms and charges

Why does the removal of electrons from a substance leave it electrically charged?

All substances are made up of atoms. For example, water is made up of oxygen atoms and hydrogen atoms. In turn, atoms are made up of even smaller particles:

- **electrons**, which have a negative electric charge
- **protons**, which have a positive electric charge
- **neutrons**, which are neutral (they have no electric charge).

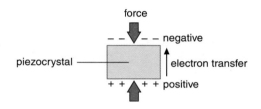

The transfer of electrons causes the ends of the crystal to become oppositely charged.

The protons and neutrons cluster together at the centre of the atom and form its nucleus. The nucleus is heavy, very small and positively charged. The electrons occupy the rest of the space of the atom.

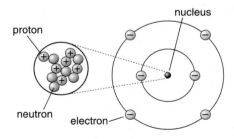

This picture represents a single carbon atom. The nucleus is so small that it has been enlarged to show the particles inside it.

? Things to do

1. A lithium atom has four neutrons and three protons. Draw a picture to show the particles in one lithium atom.

2. State the type of charge on each of these particles: electron, proton, neutron, atom.

Friction charging EH3

All atoms are neutral overall. This is because they contain the same number of protons and electrons. So the positive charge of the nucleus exactly cancels out the negative charge of the electrons around it.

Suppose that one of the electrons is removed. This leaves more protons than electrons, so the atom is now positively charged. It has become a **positive ion**. Similarly, if an atom picks up an extra electron it becomes a **negative ion**.

So if two different materials are rubbed against each other, electrons can be transferred from one to the other. The one that gains electrons becomes negative. The one that loses electrons becomes positive.

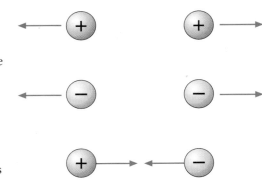

Only opposite charges attract each other.

Things with opposite charge attract each other.

Things with the same charge repel each other.

Materials often become charged when they are rubbed against each other. For example, glass becomes positive when it is rubbed with a silk cloth. The cloth removes electrons from the glass, so the cloth becomes negative.

You can become charged too! On a car journey, as your clothes rub against the car seats, electric charge may be transferred. Most parts inside the car are made of insulating plastics or fabrics, so the charge builds up on you. When you step out of the car, and touch the ground or the conducting metal body of the car, the charge leaks away and you may feel an electric shock.

Things to do

1   A silk cloth is rubbed on a sheet of glass. Carefully explain why they stick to each other afterwards.

2   Cut two thin strips of tissue paper. Put them together and hold one end. Run your other hand down the strips, with one finger between them. Explain what happens.

Avoiding explosions

Wherever insulators rub against each other, static electric charges may build up. When they are discharged, they may cause sparks.

It is very easy for a tiny spark to ignite a flammable gas! This is useful when you want to light a gas stove, but can be lethal in lots of other situations. Here are two examples.

- Sailors on ocean-going oil tankers wear shoes with conducting soles. This stops them becoming charged as they walk about, so there are no sparks that might ignite any oil vapour.

- Before an aeroplane is fuelled, it is connected to the fuel tanker by a metal strap. This allows electrons to flow safely between the two, neutralising any charge that the aeroplane may pick up as fuel rushes into it.

If static charges build up when an aeroplane is refuelling the sparks caused could ignite the fuel and cause a catastrophic explosion.

Discharging safely

Sparks from static electricity can easily destroy electronic circuits. People who work in the electronics industry often have to wear metal bracelets connected by metal wires to the ground. This provides an easy route for electrons to discharge any static electricity generated by friction with the floor.

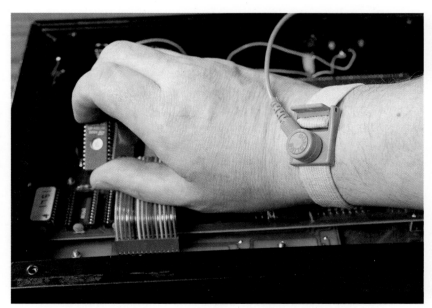

This person can't get charged up and damage the electronic components they are touching. The surface of the bench is made of a conducting material.

3 Making use of static electricity

Lightning

A lightning flash is just a very big spark! Air currents in a storm cloud result in a build-up of electrons. The lightning flash happens when electrons suddenly transfer from the cloud to the ground. The lightning discharges the cloud, leaving it neutral.

You may see smaller sparks being made by a spark machine (for example, a Van de Graaff generator). The friction of a moving belt produces a large charge, which can be discharged suddenly, causing a spark.

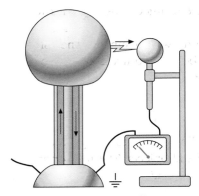

You can use a Van de Graaff generator to create a miniature lightning flash!

Things to do

Use the idea of electrons, conductors and insulators to answer these questions.

1   Some of the gases doctors use in anesthetics are flammable. Explain why the floors of hospital operating theatres are made of a conducting material.

2   Carpets in offices with computers sometimes have metal wires threaded in them. Suggest why.

Useful static

Static electricity may be hazardous, but it can also be very useful. It can be used to clean smoke from power stations, to make printers work and to help paint metal objects efficiently. Many useful applications of static electricity rely on the fact that neutral objects are often attracted to charged ones.

'Neutral' attraction

Can you make a balloon stick to the wall? First, rub it on your jumper – this will give the balloon a charge of static electricity. But why does it stick to the wall, which is neutral?

The charge on the balloon affects electrons in the wall, making them move so that the wall gets a charge that is opposite to the charge on the balloon.

In the same way, if you comb your hair with a plastic comb, the comb will then pick up tiny pieces of tissue paper. The charge on the comb **induces** an opposite charge on the paper.

The charged balloons 'stick' to the wall.

Smoke cleaning

Power stations use static electricity to clean their smoke. Charged metal rods are placed in the path of the smoke. The neutral particles of ash are attracted to the charged rods and stick to them. Once the rods are covered with ash they are removed and hit with hammers. The ash falls off and can be used to make cement or thermal insulation.

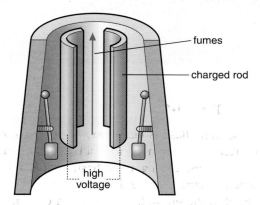

Air pollution from power stations is reduced by removing smoke and ash particles from the fumes.

Spraying paint

Static electricity allows paint to be sprayed efficiently onto metal objects. The metal nozzle of the spray gun is positively charged by a power supply, so it strips electrons off the paint as it emerges. The charged droplets of spray are attracted to any object that is connected to earth. As the droplets land on the object they are neutralised.

Photocopying

Photocopiers and laser printers use static electricity to print onto paper. They use **selenium**, which is an insulator in the dark and a conductor in the light. This is how it's done:

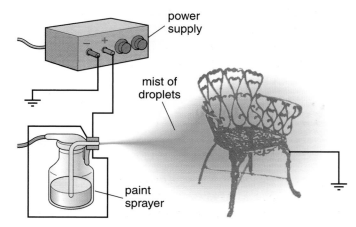

The charged droplets of paint repel each other, giving the object an even coat.

- the selenium plate is given a small positive charge
- an image of the page to be copied is shone on the selenium – where light arrives on the plate, the charge leaks away
- a fine powder (toner) is sprinkled on the plate. It only sticks to charged parts of the plate
- after loose **toner** is shaken off, paper with a strong positive charge is put on the plate
- the toner from the plate sticks to the paper
- the paper is heated to melt the toner into place.

? Things to do

3 Suggest why furniture polish is made so that it is slightly conducting.

4 Clean hair is an insulator. Explain why clean hair tends to stand on end when it is combed.

4 Electricity on the move

Electric charge and current (SS) EH5

Instead of making sparks with a Van de Graaff generator, the charge can be made to flow away smoothly through a wire. A meter shows that there is an **electric current** in the wire as the charge flows away. A flow of charge is called a current.

The unit used to measure electric current is the **ampere** (A), or 'amp', and meters that measure current are called **ammeters**. The unit used for measuring electric charge is the **coulomb** (C). One coulomb of charge is transferred when a current of one ampere flows for one second.

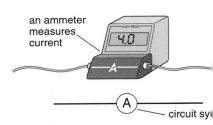

an ammeter measures current

circuit sy

This is an ammeter and its circuit symbol.

F

$$Q = It$$

The quantity of charge, Q (in coulombs), is equal to the current, I (in amperes), multiplied by the time, t (in seconds), for which the current flows.

Electric circuits

An electric current needs a conducting pathway, or **circuit**, to carry it. One of the simplest devices with an electric circuit in it is a torch. You can make an equivalent circuit using a cell, a bulb and two wires.

The chemicals in the cell make one end positive and the other end negative. Electrons forced out of the negative end flow through the metal wires and bulb filament, back to the positive end of the cell.

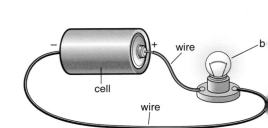

This is what the circuit is like inside a torch.

Closed and open circuits

Make sure you understand why two wires are needed in the torch circuit above. Current must flow all *round* the circuit and *back* to the cell – this is called a **closed circuit**. A switch is a device for opening up a gap in a circuit to stop the current. The circuit is then 'open' – the path is not complete and no current flows.

Conventional current

When electricity was first discovered, scientists knew that *something* had to be moving all the way round a circuit. The direction of this **conventional current** is shown with arrows on circuit diagrams. Electrons actually flow the other way!

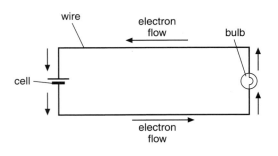

The cell makes electrons flow around the circuit, which causes electric current.

?

Things to do

1   The current in a resistor is 5 A. Calculate how much charge flows in (or out of) it in an hour.

2   Charge flows out of a cell at a rate of 15 C per minute. Calculate the current in the cell.

Series circuits

The circuits shown below are **series** circuits. There is only one pathway for the current. Current must flow through the whole series of components.

 The current is the same all the way round a series circuit.

Resistance (SS) EH7, EH8, EH9, EH10

Even the best conductors offer some **resistance** to electric current. Sometimes devices are deliberately made to have large resistance.

For example, the filament of a bulb is made of very thin wire so that it has a higher resistance. The energy transferred as current passes through this resistance heats the filament so that it glows brightly – you can feel the heat from a working bulb.

Resistors are components made from materials that are not very good conductors. When they are added to a circuit, the extra resistance limits the size of the current. The unit used to measure resistance is the **ohm**.

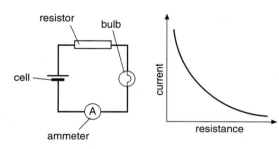

The current in the bulb goes down as the resistor in the circuit is replaced by larger and larger ones.

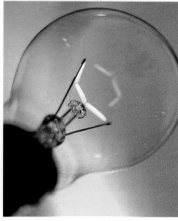

The high resistance of the filament means that more energy is transferred as the electric current passes through.

Current control

Some devices are made so that their resistance can be varied. Here are some examples:

- A **variable resistor** has a knob that allows the resistance to be adjusted by hand. Turning the knob changes the resistance. Variable resistors are used in volume controls on radios.
- A **light dependent resistor** (LDR) has a very high resistance in the dark. Its resistance drops to a low value when light is shone on it. An LDR can be used in the circuit to control automatic street lights.
- The resistance of a **thermistor** gets smaller as its temperature goes up. A thermistor can vary the resistance in a thermostat circuit to control central heating.

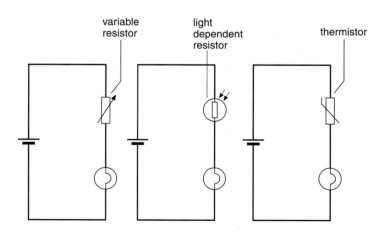

Devices whose resistance can be varied are very useful in control systems.

5 Voltage and energy

Electric current and energy transfer

If current isn't used up in a circuit, then what is? The answer is **energy**. Of course, 'used up' isn't the right expression, because energy can never be created or destroyed. Instead, electrical energy is *transferred* to other forms – bulbs produce light (and heat), motors produce movement, and so on.

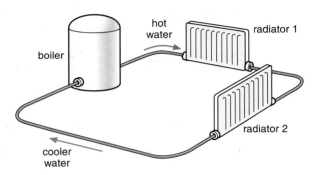

There are lots of similarities between a heating system circuit and an electric circuit in the way energy is transferred.

Heating system	Electric circuit
the *boiler* supplies energy to heat up the water *pipes* carry the water round – the flow is the same at every point	the *cell* provides electrical potential energy *wires* carry the current – the current is the same at every point
radiators transfer energy	*bulbs* or other devices transfer energy
the *temperature* of the water gets lower as it goes round	the *electrical potential energy* is used up as current flows in each component

Voltage (SS) EH17, EH18

You can think of the **voltage** of a cell or other electrical supply as the driving force that causes the electric current to flow. In a given circuit, the larger the voltage, the larger the current.

Voltages are always measured as voltage *differences* between two points in a circuit (for example, between the two ends of a cell, or across a component in the circuit).

Since voltage measures the *electrical potential energy*, it is sometimes referred to as **potential difference (p.d.)**.

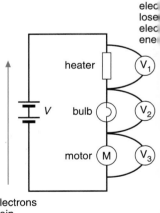

electrons gain electrical energy

*The voltmeter is connected in **para** with the part of the circuit where t voltage difference is being measure*

The amount of energy transferred by charge as it travels in a circuit is given by the formula:

$$E = QV$$

where E = energy, in joules (J)

Q = quantity of charge, in coulombs (C)

V = potential difference, in volts (V)

Sharing voltages

Remember that the *current* in a series circuit will be the *same* all the way round. However, some of the energy carried by the current is transferred by each component in the circuit. The remaining energy gets less – that is, the *voltage falls*.

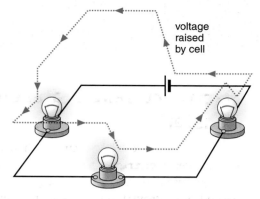

Resistance and current EH19

Each part of an electric circuit has some resistance to the current. The amount of current that can be produced by a given voltage is limited by the total resistance of the circuit.

Voltage falls in each appliance as energy is transferred.

The resistance of a circuit can be worked out from measurements of the voltage applied and the current that is produced. Resistance is measured in units called ohms (Ω).

$$V = IR$$

where V = potential difference, in volts (V)

I = current, in amperes (A)

R = resistance, in ohms (Ω)

Example: When a 12 V battery is connected to a bulb, the current in the circuit is 2 A. What is the resistance of the bulb?

voltage, V = current, I × resistance, R

$$R = \frac{12}{2} = 6 \text{ ohms}$$

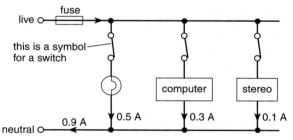

Devices that run from the mains voltage are not connected in series (think of two reasons why not). They are connected so that each one is in a *separate* branch of the circuit. This is called connecting in **parallel**.

When you plug several devices into the mains, you are connecting them in parallel rather than in series.

In series circuits:

- there is only one single pathway for the current
- a switch, or break, at any point stops the current to all devices in the circuit
- resistances of components in series add up to give the total resistance for the circuit
- voltage is shared – there is a voltage drop across each component.

In parallel circuits:

- there is more than one pathway for current
- each branch receives the full voltage
- each branch can be switched separately
- the current in common parts of the circuit is the sum of the currents in each branch.

? Things to do

1   A lamp draws a current of 0.5 A from a 230 V supply. What is the resistance of the lamp?

2   A battery provides a current of 0.6 A through a resistance of 50 ohms. What is the voltage of the battery?

3   Three resistors, with resistances 4 Ω, 8 Ω and 12 Ω are in series. The current in the circuit is 0.5 A. Calculate:

   a the voltage across each resistor   b the total voltage across all three resistors.

6 Calculating the cost

Watts make the kettle quicker

Mains electric devices carry a sign to show their power.
Power is the rate at which electrical energy is transferred.

To work out the power of a device, you need to know two
things. The current tells you how much charge is transferred
per second, and the voltage tells you how much energy is
transferred by each coulomb of charge. Together, they tell you
how fast energy is transferred when the device is working.
Electric power is measured in **watts**.

We'll have to get a more powerful kettle – this one takes too long to boil the water!

$P = IV$

where P = power of the device, in watts (W)

I = current, in amperes (A)

V = voltage, in volts (V)

Example: The bulb in a car headlamp takes a
current of 4 A. The battery voltage is 12 V.
Calculate the power of the headlamp.

power, P = current, I × voltage, V

$= 4 \times 12$

$= 48$ W

The watt is a very small unit of power. For most devices that
operate from mains voltage, it is more convenient to use kilowatts
(1 kW = 1000 W). So, for example, a 500 W microwave oven has
a power of 0.5 kW.

The power of an average car headlamp is under 50 watts.

Kilowatt-hours

The electricity you use has to be paid for! You actually pay for the
amount of energy used. To work out the amount of energy
transferred by a device, you need to know its power (the rate
of transfer of energy) and how long it was used for.

$E = PT$

where E = energy used, in kilowatt-hours (kWh)

P = power, in kilowatts (kW)

t = time, in hours (h)

Example: If you leave a 100 W light on for 24
hours, how much electricity do you use?

energy used, E = power, P × time, t

$= \dfrac{100}{1000} \times 24$

$= 0.1 \times 24 = 2.4$ kWh

The price of electricity is quoted as so much per **kilowatt-hour (kWh)**.

Electricity costs about 9p per kilowatt-hour, so leaving the light on would
cost 9 × 2.4 = 21.6 pence.

Choosing cables

Every part of a circuit has some resistance, even the wires in the lead. The energy used to overcome this resistance is transferred as heat, so circuits warm up while they are in use. Sometimes it is a nuisance, and sometimes it can be dangerous! Overheating of electric wiring has caused many house fires. So you need to use the right lead for each purpose.

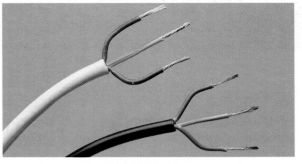

3 A and 13 A cable: which is the right one to use?

Fuses (SS) EH23

Sometimes the insulation round wires breaks, and the wires touch, making a shorter route for the current. Because this 'short circuit' has less resistance, a bigger current flows. A fuse is a thin piece of tin wire. Too much current makes the fuse heat up and melt, breaking the circuit and stopping the current.

The mains plug on each device has a fuse, which forms part of the 'live' wire.

3 A and 13 A fuses: which is the right one to fit?

Choosing fuses

The general purpose fuses fitted in mains lead plugs are usually either 3 A or 13 A. How do you choose which to use?

In Britain, all mains devices operate from a 220–240 V supply. If you know the power of the device (shown on the label) you can work out how much current it takes when working normally.

Example: What is the power of a mains device that takes a current of 3 A?

power, P = current, I × voltage, V

power = 3 × 230 = 720 W

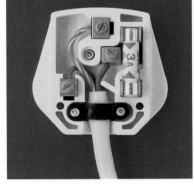

Fuses break the circuit if the current flowing gets too large.

? Things to do

1 Work out the power of a mains device which takes a current of 13 amperes.

2 For each of the devices in the picture, work out

   a the current that it takes when working normally

   b which type of fuse to use

   c the cost of using it for 30 minutes, if electricity costs 9p per kWh.

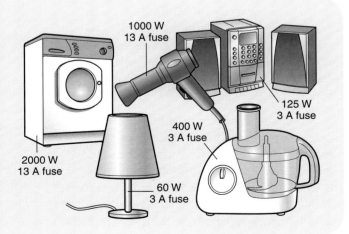

1000 W
13 A fuse

125 W
3 A fuse

400 W
3 A fuse

2000 W
13 A fuse

60 W
3 A fuse

Down to earth for safety

All electric circuits need two wires, but if you look inside the plug on many devices, you will see three wires! The brown (live) wire and the blue (neutral) wire carry electricity in and out of the device. The green and yellow wire (striped so that even colour-blind people can see it easily) is the earth wire. Every mains device that has exposed metal parts must have an earth wire. It is connected to the outer case of the device.

compressor

If the wiring inside this fridge is correct and in good condition, the electric circuit involves just the live and neutral wires. The earth wire does nothing.

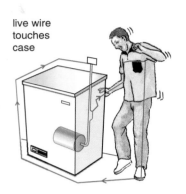

live wire touches case

If there is no earth wire and the live wire becomes worn or damaged so that it touches the metal case, you could be electrocuted. When you touch the case, your body becomes part of the electric circuit.

This fridge has an earth wire. If a damaged live wire touches the case, it forms a closed circuit with the earth lead. A large current flows in this circuit and the fuse in the mains plug melts. This breaks the circuit, so the fridge is safe to touch. You can now have the fault fixed!

Circuit breakers

Circuit breakers use the magnetic effect of electric current. Residual current circuit breakers have live and return wires wound together into a coil. As long as the current flowing into the circuit is equal to that flowing out through the return wire, the two magnetic fields exactly cancel out (the currents are flowing in opposite directions round the coil). If they become unbalanced (because current is leaking to earth, or through some unfortunate user!) there will be an unbalanced magnetic field, and the connection is tripped out (broken).

Circuit breakers act faster than fuses, and so give increased protection. Also, they can be more convenient. If a fuse melts, it has to be mended or replaced. Circuit breakers simply operate a switch. The circuit can be reconnected simply by pushing a button on the circuit breaker (but you should try to locate the faulty apparatus and disconnect it first!).

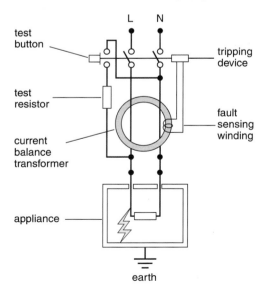

test button

test resistor

current balance transformer

appliance

L N

tripping device

fault sensing winding

earth

A circuit breaker uses the magnetic effect of electric current to break the circuit if the current gets too large.

Double insulation

The wires inside a device are insulated. Many devices also have an outer casing made entirely of plastic, with no metal parts exposed. The casing forms an extra layer of insulation to protect you.

These devices are said to be **double insulated**, and they do not need an earth wire.

Double insulated devices have a label showing this sign.

Ring mains

The wall sockets in your house are probably wired using a ring main. This has a live wire and a neutral wire, which each run all round the circuit and back to the supply. Each wall socket is wired across from the live wire to the neutral.

Because the wires run both ways round the house, current can flow either way, which doubles the current that can be carried safely. This also makes sure that all the sockets are in parallel, so each works independently of the others.

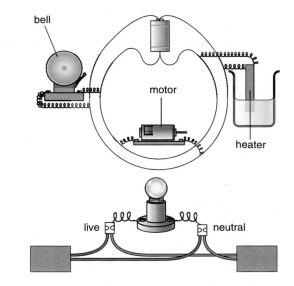

Electrical heating

- In **radiant heaters**, a coil of wire wound round a support is heated by the current (often to red-hot). The energy is given out mostly as infrared radiation. A reflector behind the heating element directs the radiation into the room.

- **Immersion heaters** have a heating element in a waterproof casing so that it can be immersed in the water that is to be heated.

- In **microwave cookers**, a small transmitter sends microwaves through the food. Water absorbs microwaves, and the energy absorbed heats the food.

When you plug in devices at home, they are automatically connected in parallel, because of the ring main system.

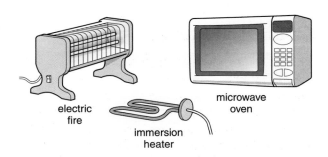

Electricity is used in many ways for heating.

? Things to do

1. Explain why it may be unsafe to use a lead from one type of device to supply a different one.

2. Explain how the earth wire, fuse and a circuit breaker could work together to protect both you and the machine from harm if a bare wire in your washing machine touches the outer casing.

3. In an electric cooker, the oven, grill and hotplates all contain elements that are heated by electric current. For each of these, describe how energy reaches the food to heat it.

1 A perspex rod is rubbed against a woollen cloth. Complete this sentence:

The perspex becomes positive because _____ have transferred to the _____, giving the cloth a _____ charge.

2 Jo combs her hair with a nylon comb. Her hair stands on end afterwards and the comb has become negatively charged. Suggest why this happens.

3 An atom of carbon-14 has six protons and eight neutrons. How many electrons does it have? Draw a diagram to show the arrangement of all three particles in the atom.

4 Sailors on ocean-going tankers wear shoes with conducting soles. Explain why. Use ideas about static electricity.

5 Containers for storing large quantities of petrol are always made of metal. Suggest and explain why using plastic containers could be dangerous.

6 Small pieces of neutral paper are attracted to objects that have *either* negative *or* positive charge. Use the idea of particles in atoms to explain why.

7 The electrical equipment in this car is supplied with energy from a 12 V battery.

a Describe how a flow of electrons transfers energy from the battery to the headlights. Draw an energy arrow diagram to show the energy transfers involved.

b One of the headlamp bulbs takes a current of 5.5 A. How much charge flows in an hour when the lamp is on?

c The car has two headlamps. Explain why they are connected in parallel.

d When the car is started, the battery transfers a charge of 72 C through the starter motor in 6 seconds. Calculate the current in the motor.

e In some of the electric circuits in the car, the resistance needs to vary as conditions change. Find and copy the symbols used in circuit diagrams for each of these devices, and explain how the resistance of each one can be altered:

i a variable resistor

ii an LDR

iii a thermistor.

8 Explain why high voltage electrical supplies are more dangerous than low voltage supplies.

9 A set of Christmas tree lights has 23 bulbs in series. It is supplied from the mains (220–240 V).

a The label on each bulb says '10 V, 2.5 W'. Explain why the working voltage for each bulb is so much less than the supply voltage.

b Explain why all of the bulbs are equally bright when they are switched on.

c Explain what will happen if one bulb breaks.

10 A 4.5 V battery produces a current of 1.5 A through a bulb.

a Calculate the resistance of the bulb.

b What current would be supplied if a second bulb was added, in series with the first?

c How would this affect the brightness of the bulbs?

d Write out the names of the units used for voltage, current and resistance.

11 Explain how you would measure the resistance of a motor connected to a battery. Include a circuit diagram.

12 A 200 W computer, a 1.5 kW heater and a 500 W lamp are all run off the same extension lead connected to the 230 V mains. Calculate the value of the fuse required in the lead.

13 A physics textbook says, 'Fuses protect the wiring in equipment, circuit breakers protect the user'. Explain this, and describe how fuses and circuit breakers work.

INTRODUCING
Mining and minerals

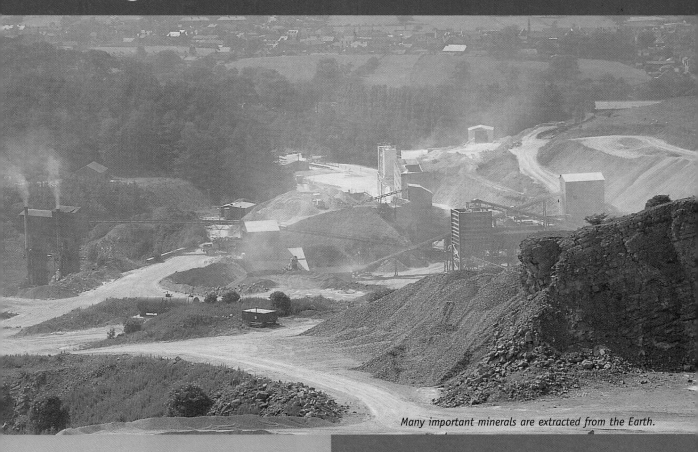

Many important minerals are extracted from the Earth.

ry these first

Which gas is formed when calcium carbonate reacts with dilute acid?

Which elements are combined in calcium carbonate?

Calcium hydroxide contains three elements. Which three elements?

Which gas is formed when magnesium reacts with dilute sulphuric acid?

Which three metals react with cold water?

Which two metals are stored under oil?

Which three metals do not react with water or steam?

Which metal is most likely to be found uncombined in the Earth?

What is special about the order of metals in the list?

Which metal in the list rusts?

Potassium K
Sodium Na
Calcium Ca
Magnesium Mg
Zinc Zn
Iron Fe
Lead Pb
Copper Cu

In this unit you will learn:

- that metals are found in the ground
- that compounds of metals are called minerals and these are found in ores
- that metals high in the reactivity series are extracted by electrolysis
- that metals in the middle of the reactivity series are extracted by reduction usually with carbon
- that metals at the bottom of the reactivity series are extracted by just heating or may be found uncombined in the ground
- that electrolysis of salt solution can produce a range of useful materials
- that sulphur dioxide, produced by roasting some ores, can be used to produce sulphuric acid
- that calculations can be done to work out masses of chemicals reacting and produced.

1 Why are minerals important?

Minerals as raw materials MM1

The photograph on page 129 shows a limestone quarry in the Peak District in Derbyshire. This is an area of great natural beauty.

Rocks are usually mixtures of substances. We call each pure substance in a rock a mineral. Limestone is almost pure calcium carbonate. This means the rock is a pure mineral.

Mining companies extract other useful minerals from the ground. The rocks shown on this page contain the minerals that will be discussed in this unit. Some of the minerals are used in the form in which they are dug up, whereas others need to be processed to obtain more useful substances.

Rock salt:
- contains almost 100% sodium chloride (NaCl)
- mostly used to make chlorine, sodium hydroxide and sodium carbonate

Haematite:
- often over 85% iron oxide (Fe_2O_3)
- used as a source of iron

Limestone:
- contains almost 100% calcium carbonate ($CaCO_3$)
- used as an ingredient in cement and glass
- used for building and road making

Copper pyrites:
- contains less than 1% copper iron sulphide ($CuFeS_2$)
- used as a source of copper metal

Galena:
- contains about 15% lead sulphide (PbS)
- used as a source of lead

Bauxite:
- contains about 75% aluminium oxide (Al_2O_3) and 25% iron oxide (Fe_2O_3)
- used as a source of aluminium metal

Limestone mining (SS) MM2, MM3

Limestone was formed millions of years ago from shells of marine organisms. When the creatures died, the shells were deposited on the sea floor and as the sediments built up they gradually changed to rock. Limestone is a **sedimentary rock**. Because of earth movements and erosion, many limestone deposits are very near the surface and can easily be dug out of the ground.

Every year 100 million tonnes of limestone are mined in the United Kingdom. This leaves some very large holes in the ground. Why is so much mined?

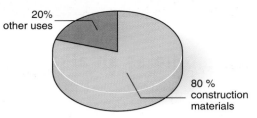

total UK production = 97 million tonnes

20% other uses

80 % construction materials

This chart shows the main uses of limestone.

What is limestone used for?

 (SS) MM4

The pie chart above shows that most of the limestone mined is used for construction materials. The quarry produces crushed stone of various sizes. These are known as 'aggregate', which is the engineer's name for small pieces of rock. Aggregate is used where a solid foundation is needed such as under concrete floors, roads and railway tracks.

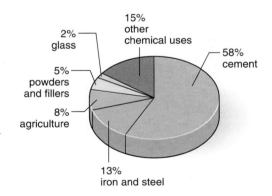

Limestone aggregate is used to construct railway tracks.

The pie chart to the right shows how the remaining 20% of the limestone mined is used.

Limestone is used as an aggregate because it has appropriate physical properties and there is a lot of it available so it is relatively cheap. In all of the uses shown in the second pie chart, the limestone – or a substance called quicklime that is made from it – is taking part in chemical reactions.

2% glass

15% other chemical uses

5% powders and fillers

58% cement

8% agriculture

13% iron and steel

This chart shows uses of limestone other than for aggregate.

?

Things to do

Use the information next to the pictures of minerals to answer the following questions.

1   Which of the minerals is often used in the form in which it is dug out of the ground?

2   Which mineral is the source of an important non-metal?

3   Aluminium is more abundant in the Earth's crust than iron, but it is a more expensive metal. Suggest why this is so.

Limestone as an alkali

Limestone is used to produce a cheap alkali, which can be used to neutralise soil that is too acidic. Certain crops, such as cabbages, do not grow well in acidic soil.

When limestone is heated it decomposes. Calcium oxide (sometimes called quicklime) and carbon dioxide are formed:

$$CaCO_3 \rightarrow CaO + CO_2$$

A vigorous reaction occurs when water is added to calcium oxide. The reaction is very exothermic and the heat given out converts some of the added water to steam.

calcium oxide + water $\rightarrow$ calcium hydroxide

$$CaO + H_2O \rightarrow Ca(OH)_2$$

Calcium hydroxide (slaked lime) is a cheap alkali. It is slightly soluble in water and its solution (limewater) is used to test for carbon dioxide.

Farmers use slaked lime or limestone to make the soil less acidic.

How much quicklime can you make?

The plant manager of a kiln needs to be able to calculate how much limestone to heat to produce the required amount of quicklime. The basis for the calculation is the equation:

$$CaCO_3 \rightarrow CaO + CO_2$$

Each formula tells you the relative number of atoms of each element in the compound. For example, CO_2 shows that there are twice as many oxygen atoms as carbon atoms in carbon dioxide.

Before you can work out how much of a compound would be made (or used up) in a chemical change, you need to know how heavy the different types of atom are, compared to one another.

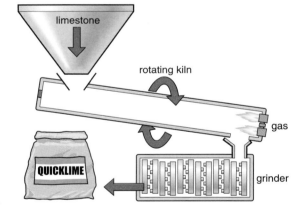

Limestone is heated on a large scale in a rotating kiln to produce quicklime.

Comparing the masses of atoms

For example, carbon atoms are 12 times as heavy as hydrogen atoms. Oxygen atoms are 16 times as heavy as hydrogen atoms and calcium atoms are 40 times as heavy as hydrogen atoms. Scientists use a 'relative atomic mass scale', on which hydrogen atoms have a **relative atomic mass (RAM)** of 1, carbon atoms a RAM of 12 and calcium atoms a RAM of 40.

The relative atomic mass scale is used to compare the masses of atoms of different elements.

On this scale, the relative atomic mass (RAM) of carbon is 12.

Relative formula mass

The formula of limestone, calcium carbonate, is $CaCO_3$. This shows that for every calcium atom in calcium carbonate there is one carbon atom and three oxygen atoms. You can use the same relative mass scale that we used for atoms to find the **relative formula mass** of a compound. For example, the relative atomic masses of calcium, carbon and oxygen are:

Ca = 40, C = 12, O = 16.

So, the relative formula mass of $CaCO_3$ = 40 + 12 + 16 + 16 + 16 = 100

Check that you understand why the relative formula mass of CaO is 56 and that of CO_2 is 44.

The relative formula mass of a substance is found by adding together the relative atomic masses of all of the atoms in the formula of the substance.

Relative formula mass is often called **relative molecular mass**.

Reacting masses

The plant manager can use relative formula masses to work out how much limestone to use to make quicklime by putting the relative formula masses under the formulas in the equation for the reaction:

$CaCO_3 \rightarrow CaO + CO_2$

100   56   44

This means that 100 tonnes of calcium carbonate (limestone) need to be heated to make 56 tonnes of calcium oxide (quicklime).

Things to do

1 Calculate the relative formula masses of each of the following compounds:

   a water, H_2O b copper(II) oxide, CuO   c iron(III) oxide, Fe_2O_3

   d sulphuric acid, H_2SO_4 e calcium hydroxide, $Ca(OH)_2$

2 What mass of limestone must be heated to meet a production target of 4480 tonnes of quicklime per month?

3 What mass of carbon dioxide would be produced at the same time as the 4480 tonnes of quicklime?

4 Quicklime is usually converted to slaked lime (calcium hydroxide) by reacting it with water:

   $CaO + H_2O \rightarrow Ca(OH)_2$

   What mass of calcium hydroxide (slaked lime) could be made from 4480 tonnes of quicklime?

5 Draw a table like this and use a copy of the Periodic Table to help you complete it.

Name of element	Symbol for element	Relative atomic mass
hydrogen	C	12
carbon		
oxygen		
sodium		
...		

Extracting metals from minerals (SS) MM6, MM7

A rock that contains a useful mineral is sometimes called an **ore**.

When a mineral is found, a decision has to be made about whether to extract it or not.

The decision may be influenced by:

- scientific evidence – *How much of the useful mineral does the ore contain?*
- technical evidence – *How easy is it to separate the mineral?*
- market predictions – *What is the likely demand for the product?*
- environmental and social factors – *How will it affect the environment and the local community?*

Metal is extracted from a mineral. Minerals are contained in ores.

Some of the possible benefits and drawbacks of mining ores are shown in this table.

Benefits	Drawbacks
more jobs	spoils the appearance of the countryside
produces useful materials	harms plant and animal life
creates wealth for the company and community	leaves waste that requires disposal

Metals occur in nature chemically combined with different elements:

- sodium and magnesium are found as chlorides
- aluminium and iron are found as oxides
- zinc, lead and copper are found as sulphides.

Gold, however, occurs in some rocks just as pure gold, uncombined with any other element.

We have to use chemical reactions to obtain the metals. If the mineral is a sulphide – such as lead sulphide, PbS (galena) – it is first heated in air to convert it to an oxide. In the case of lead, the oxide can then be converted to the metal by heating it with carbon.

? Things to do

1   When a new deposit of mineral is found, before spending a large amount of money digging up the mineral, the mining company needs to know how much metal they will get from it.

   a If 500 000 tonnes of a copper ore could be extracted and it contained, on average, 0.5% of a copper oxide (CuO) mineral, what is the maximum mass of copper that could be extracted?

   b If copper sells for £2000 per tonne, how much would this copper be worth?

   Relative atomic masses: $Cu = 64$, $O = 16$.

Representing reactions

We can use **equations** to represent the chemical changes (**reactions**) that have occurred. For example, when lead oxide is mixed with carbon and heated, the reaction can be represented by this **word equation**:

lead oxide + carbon → lead + carbon dioxide

This shows all the substances used in the reaction (**reactants**) and all those that are formed (**products**). An even shorter way to represent the reaction is to use a **symbol equation**:

$2PbO + C \rightarrow 2Pb + CO_2$

In a chemical change, atoms are not created or destroyed, but just rearranged to form new substances. This is shown by this equation. Count the number of atoms of each element on each side of the equation to check there is the same number. This is a **balanced equation**.

Balanced symbol equations have the same number of atoms of each element on each side.

What type of reaction is this?

If you can recognise similarities between reactions, and so classify them as a particular type of reaction, that makes it easier to remember them. For example, as well as lead, the metals zinc and copper can also be obtained from their oxides by heating them with carbon:

$ZnO + C \rightarrow Zn + CO$

$2CuO + C \rightarrow Cu + CO_2$

In all three reactions, oxygen is *taken away* from the metal oxide, leaving the metal.

A compound is **reduced** if oxygen is removed from it.

A reaction where a compound has oxygen removed from it is called a **reduction** reaction.

A substance that removes the oxygen is called a **reducing agent**.

Things to do

2   Write a word equation for the reaction of copper(II) oxide with carbon.

3   Copy and complete these sentences.

   a The copper(II) oxide has been _____ to copper.

   b This is an example of a _____ reaction.

   c The reducing agent was _____.

Your teacher may show you the reduction of copper oxide and how to use the results to work out the formula of the copper oxide.

Iron is extracted from iron ore in a **blast furnace** using a reduction reaction. A mixture of iron ore, containing iron(III) oxide (Fe_2O_3), coke (C) and limestone ($CaCO_3$) is loaded into the top of the furnace. It is called a blast furnace because a blast of hot air is forced in at the bottom.

What happens in the blast furnace?

The coke burns in the oxygen in the hot air:

$$C + O_2 \rightarrow CO_2 \qquad [1]$$

This reaction is exothermic, giving out a lot of heat.

At higher temperatures, carbon dioxide reacts with more coke to give carbon monoxide:

$$CO_2 + C \rightarrow 2CO \qquad [2]$$

The carbon monoxide takes the oxygen from the iron oxide, which is reduced to iron:

$$Fe_2O_3 + 3CO \rightarrow 2Fe + 3CO_2 \qquad [3]$$

The furnace is so hot that the iron is liquid. It sinks to the bottom of the furnace, from where it can be tapped off.

The blast furnace.

The limestone is there to react with impurities in the iron ore. First it is decomposed by heat:

$$CaCO_3 \rightarrow CaO + CO_2 \qquad [4]$$

The calcium oxide reacts with impurities, mainly sand (silicon dioxide, SiO_2). It forms a **slag** that floats on top of the liquid iron.

$$CaO + SiO_2 \rightarrow CaSiO_3 \qquad [5]$$

? Things to do

1 Copy out symbol equation [3].

   a Which compound in the equation has been reduced?

   b Which compound has caused the reduction (that is, which is the reducing agent)?

2 Which equation shows a reaction in the blast furnace that is exothermic?

3 In which equation is decomposition occurring?

4 What mass of iron could be made from 320 tonnes of iron(III) oxide (Fe_2O_3)? Relative atomic masses: Fe = 56, O = 16.

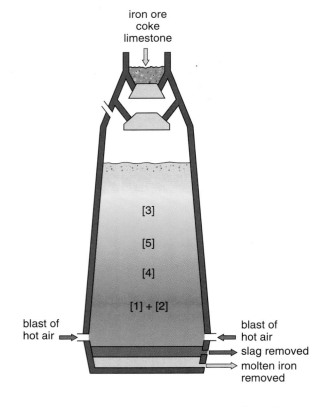

iron ore
coke
limestone

[3]

[5]

[4]

[1] + [2]

blast of hot air →   ← blast of hot air
→ slag removed
→ molten iron removed

How the blast furnace works. The numbers refer to the equations in the text.

Making steel MM8

Iron from the blast furnace is impure. It contains carbon, silicon and phosphorus. They are burned away by blowing oxygen into the molten iron. They are oxidised.

Pure iron is too brittle for many uses. Measured amounts of carbon are added back to the liquid iron. The metal produced is called steel. Different percentages of carbon give the steel different properties and so make it suitable for different uses.

A metal that has been made by mixing liquid metals together is called an **alloy**. For example, brass is an alloy of copper (70%) and zinc (30%).

Steel is an alloy even though carbon is a non-metal. Some steels do contain other metals. Stainless steel is the most well-known example. It contains about 20% chromium and 10% nickel. It is particularly useful as it does not rust, and is therefore used for cutlery and kitchen utensils.

Some car exhaust pipes are made of stainless steel. They are more expensive than mild steel (0.2% carbon), but they last a lot longer.

> Alloys are used where the properties of the mixture are superior to the properties of the individual metals. It may also be cheaper to use an alloy rather than a pure metal. For example, 'silver' coins in the UK no longer contain silver – they are an alloy of copper and nickel. 'Copper' coins are made from an alloy of copper, zinc and tin.
>
> If you look at a copy of the Periodic Table you will see that most of the metals present in these alloys are transition metals.

Rusting of iron and steel

Rusting takes place when both oxygen (or air) and water are in contact with iron or steel.

Iron is made by reducing iron oxide. Rusting is the reverse of this process. Oxygen, in the presence of water, converts the iron back to iron oxide (rust). Because oxygen has been added to the iron, rusting is an **oxidation reaction**.

Rusting can be prevented in several ways:

- coating the metal with oil and grease
- painting
- coating with plastic
- coating with zinc (galvanising)
- putting the iron or steel in contact with a more reactive metal such as magnesium, which will corrode in preference to iron rusting – this is called 'sacrificial protection'.

This steel furnace can make 600 tonnes of steel in an hour.

? Things to do

5. Write a word equation for the rusting of iron.
6. What type of reaction is rusting?
7. Find out which of the following are alloys and which are elements: brass, copper, iron, gold, bronze, duralium, lead, solder.

The thermit process

Zinc, iron, lead and copper can all be obtained by reducing the metal oxide, by heating it with carbon. The carbon *takes away* the oxygen from the oxide. Another way of removing the oxygen from a metal oxide is to heat it with a more reactive metal.

Iron can be made by heating a mixture of iron(III) oxide and aluminium. A **displacement** reaction occurs because aluminium is more reactive than iron and so takes the oxygen away from the iron:

$$Fe_2O_3 + 2Al \rightarrow Al_2O_3 + 2Fe$$

This would not be an economic process because aluminium is more expensive than iron – you would not normally use a more expensive metal to produce a less expensive one. This reaction does, however, have a practical use.

Lengths of railway track are welded together on site to produce continuous rails. This gives a more comfortable ride.

A mixture of iron oxide and aluminium powder is put between the ends of the two lengths of track, with a piece of magnesium ribbon as a fuse. When the fuse is lit a reaction occurs converting the iron oxide to iron and the high temperatures weld the two lengths of track together.

Thermit process being used to reduce iron oxide to iron, to weld rail tracks together.

The activity series

The method used to extract a metal from its minerals depends upon the position of the metal in the **activity series**.

The more reactive a metal is, the more it 'likes' to form compounds. This means it is more difficult to reduce its compounds to the metal.

For example, for sodium:

$$sodium \underset{difficult}{\overset{easy}{\rightleftarrows}} sodium\ compound$$

For copper:

$$copper \underset{easy}{\overset{difficult}{\rightleftarrows}} copper\ compound$$

So you can extract copper, lead, iron and zinc by heating their minerals with carbon. You have to use a more powerful method for extracting sodium, calcium, magnesium and aluminium.

more reactive
Na
Ca
Mg   } obtained by electrolysis
Al
- - - - - - - - - - -
Zn
Fe
Pb   } obtained by heating with carbon
Cu
less reactive

More reactive metals are extracted by electrolysis, while less reactive ones can be extracted by heating with carbon.

These metals are obtained from their compounds by **electrolysis**. As the name suggests, electrolysis is a process that uses electricity to break down a compound.

An **electrolyte** is a compound that conducts electricity when it is in a liquid state (either molten or dissolved in water).

What happens during electrolysis?

 MM9

Electrolysis is the breaking down of a substance by electricity.

The table below shows the results of investigating what happens when you try to pass an electric current through other substances.

From these observations it seems that those substances listed in the table that conduct electricity will only do so when they are in a liquid form. The particles in a liquid are able to move throughout the liquid, whereas the particles in a solid are in fixed positions and are not able to move. The ability to conduct seems to be associated with the ability of the particles in the substance to move.

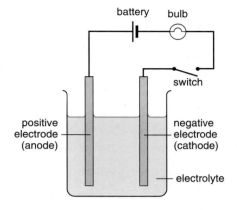

An apparatus for investigating the effects of passing an electric current through a liquid.

Compound	Does it conduct when solid?	Does it conduct when molten or dissolved in water?	What appears at the cathode (negative electrode)?	What appears at the anode (positive electrode)?
copper(II) chloride				
lead(II) bromide	✗	✓	lead	bromine
sodium chloride	✗	✓ (molten)	sodium	chlorine
aluminium oxide	✗	✓	aluminium	oxygen
poly(ethene)	✗	✗	nothing	nothing
sugar	✗	✗	nothing	nothing

Things to do

1 What results would you add to the table from your investigation of copper chloride?

2 Poly(ethene) is a compound made up of carbon and hydrogen atoms. Sugar contains carbon, hydrogen and oxygen atoms. So both of these compounds are made up entirely of non-metallic elements. All of the other compounds in the table are metals joined to non-metals.

 Look for patterns in the results.

 a What types of compounds conduct electricity?

 b Under what conditions do these compounds conduct electricity?

3 During electrolysis of substances that do conduct electricity, what type of element (metal or non-metal) appears at:

 a the positive electrode (anode)   b the negative electrode (cathode)?

6 Understanding electrolysis

Salts contain metals combined with non-metals. Melted salts conduct electricity. As it conducts, the metallic part is attracted to the negative electrode and non-metallic part to the positive electrode.

Opposite charges attract each other, so these observations indicate that the sodium particles in sodium chloride are positively charged and the chloride particles are negatively charged. These charged particles are called **ions**.

- A sodium ion has a single positive charge and is represented by Na^+.
- A chloride ion has a single negative charge and is represented by Cl^-.

In a solution of potassium manganate(VII), the potassium ions are colourless and the manganate ions are purple. When an electric current is passed through the solution, the purple manganate ions move towards the positive electrode.

Do you think manganate ions are positively or negatively charged?

What happens at the electrodes?

At the electrodes, the ions are **discharged**.

The battery is 'pushing' electrons from its negative terminal towards the negative electrode (cathode). Each sodium ion takes one electron from the negative electrode to form a sodium atom:

$$Na^+ + e^- \rightarrow Na$$

At the positive electrode (anode), each chloride ion gives one electron to the electrode. Chlorine atoms combine to form chlorine molecules (Cl_2) and chlorine gas is given off:

$$Cl^- \rightarrow Cl + e^- \qquad 2Cl \rightarrow Cl_2$$

The reactions at the electrodes remove electrons from the cathode and give electrons to the anode. Electrons move through the wire from the anode, round the circuit (via the battery) to the cathode. The circuit conducts electricity and the bulb lights up.

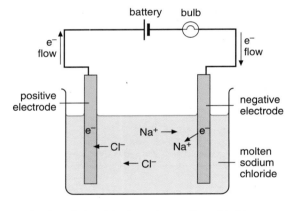

Conduction of electricity by molten sodium chloride.

The equations used to show what happens at the electrodes are called ionic half-equations. They are called half-equations because they represent half of the reaction. Another half-reaction must be occurring at the other electrode.

Some important half-equations for the discharge of ions are shown in this table.

At the negative electrode	At the positive electrode
$Na^+ + e^- \rightarrow Na$	$Cl^- \rightarrow Cl + e^-$
$Cu^{2+} + 2e^- \rightarrow Cu$	$O^{2-} \rightarrow O + 2e^-$
$Al^{3+} + 3e^- \rightarrow Al$	

Charges on ions

F

Atoms of elements are not charged – they are electrically neutral. An ion, such as Na^+, that has a single positive charge has been formed by a neutral atom losing an electron.

$$Na \rightarrow Na^+ + e^-$$

Atoms in group I of the Periodic Table (for example, lithium, sodium and potassium) have one outer electron. They form ions by giving away this electron to a non-metal. This leaves them with a single positive charge.

Li^+ Na^+ K^+

Atoms of elements in group II (for example, magnesium and calcium) have two outer electrons. They form ions with two positive charges by giving away both of these electrons to a non-metal.

Mg^{2+} Ca^{2+}

Elements in group VII of the Periodic Table (for example, chlorine, bromine and iodine) form singly charged negative ions by gaining an electron from a metal.

Cl^- Br^- I^-

Oxygen (group VI) forms oxide ions by gaining two electrons:

O^{2-}

The structure of ionic solids

When a metal and non-metal react together, electrons are transferred from metal atoms to non-metal atoms. The metal atoms become positively charged ions and the non-metal atoms become negatively charged ions.

For example, solid sodium chloride contains Na^+ ions and Cl^- ions. The opposite charges attract each other and come together to form a particular, regular arrangement or structure.

Structures of ionic compounds are called **ionic lattices**. Because the ions are unable to move, solid sodium chloride does not conduct electricity.

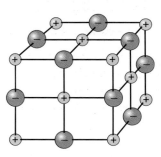

Each ion is surrounded by ions of the opposite charge. In this way, the ions are held firmly in fixed positions.

?

Things to do

1   Positive ions are sometimes called **cations** and negative ions **anions**. Explain this.

2   Write an account explaining what happens when molten calcium bromide, $CaBr_2$, is split up by electrolysis.

3   Why do you think a large amount of energy is needed to melt compounds made from ions?

4   Why do solid compounds made from ions not conduct electricity?

melting

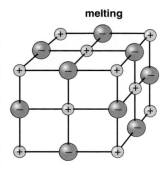

in the solid, ions are fixed in positions

heating provides enough energy to overcome the attractions between ions

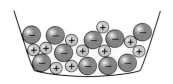

now the ions are free to move

dissolving

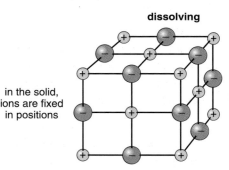

water molecules get between the ions and block the attraction

Melting or dissolving sodium chloride enables the ions to move.

7 Using electrolysis

Aluminium is a very important metal, with many uses, ranging from oven wrap and drinks cans to aircraft bodies. Aluminium is high in the activity series and has to be extracted by electrolysis.

Most soils and many rocks contain aluminium, but the only ore that can be used is bauxite (see page 130). Bauxite is an impure form of aluminium oxide (Al_2O_3). Pure aluminium oxide is white whereas bauxite contains iron(III) oxide (Fe_2O_3) which makes it a rusty brown colour.

This ore is called bauxite because it was first found near Le Baux in France.

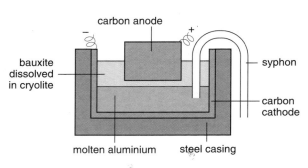

Cell for extracting aluminium.

Concentrating the ore

Bauxite usually contains about 75% of aluminium oxide with the remaining 25% being mostly iron(III) oxide. A difference in the chemical properties of these two oxides is used to separate them. Aluminium oxide dissolves in sodium hydroxide solution but iron(III) oxide does not. This is called **chemical leaching**.

First sodium hydroxide solution is added to the crushed ore. This dissolves the aluminium oxide part of the ore.

Then the mixture is filtered to separate the solution from the insoluble iron oxide.

Finally purified aluminium oxide is crystallised out of the solution.

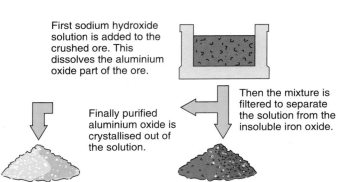

Aluminium oxide is extracted from bauxite by chemical leaching.

Extraction of aluminium

 MM11

Aluminium is extracted from aluminium oxide by electrolysis. Aluminium oxide has a very high melting point so the electrolysis of molten aluminium oxide would be too expensive, as a great deal of energy would be needed to melt it.

Less electricity is used and money is saved by mixing the aluminium oxide with a mineral called cryolite (sodium hexafluoroaluminate, Na_3AlF_6). This mixture acts as the electrolyte in the cell. It melts at a much lower temperature than aluminium oxide.

The problem is what to do with the unsightly red mud that is left after the aluminium oxide has been purified. It contains iron oxide, and is likely to be alkaline because of the presence of some sodium hydroxide.

F

Aluminium oxide is made up of Al^{3+} and O^{2-} ions.

At the negative electrode (the carbon lining of the cell), electrons are transferred from the electrode to the aluminium ions.

$$Al^{3+} + 3e^- \rightarrow Al$$

The temperature is above the melting point of aluminium. Liquid aluminium is syphoned off.

At the positive electrode (the carbon electrodes dipping into the electrolyte), electrons are transferred from the oxide ions to the electrodes. The oxygen atoms formed then combine to form O_2 gas molecules.

$$O^{2-} \rightarrow O + 2e^-$$
$$2O \rightarrow O_2$$

The hot carbon anodes have to be replaced frequently because they burn away in the oxygen produced.

$$C + O_2 \rightarrow CO_2$$

Making one tonne of aluminium

Making one tonne of aluminium requires about:

- 5 tonnes of bauxite
- 0.6 tonnes of graphite anodes
- 0.45 tonnes of fuel oil
- 0.08 tonnes of sodium hydroxide
- 0.05 tonnes of cryolite
- 17 000 kWh of electricity.

The electricity required to make one tonne of aluminium is about the same quantity produced by some power stations in one hour. A factory producing aluminium (called a **smelter**) requires a reliable source of cheap electricity.

Aluminium smelter in Anglesey, Wales.

?

Things to do

1 Suggest why:

a the purification of bauxite is usually carried out near the bauxite mine

b aluminium smelters in the UK are usually situated near the coast.

2 Draw a flow diagram to show the stages involved in obtaining aluminium metal from bauxite.

3 The formula of aluminium oxide is Al_2O_3.

a What mass of oxygen will be formed when 1 tonne of aluminium is extracted from aluminium oxide?

b If all of this oxygen combines with the carbon electrode to form carbon dioxide:

$$C + O_2 \rightarrow CO_2$$

how much carbon will be lost from the electrode?

Relative atomic masses: Al = 27, O = 16, C = 12.

Products of the salt industry

Salt – sodium chloride (NaCl) – is used to make other important chemicals, in particular sodium hydroxide, chlorine and hydrogen.

Salt occurs as halite, sometimes called rock salt. It is found in underground deposits in Cheshire. It was formed by evaporation of a shallow sea millions of years ago. The salt was then covered by other rocks.

Rock salt can be mined by the usual method of tunnelling underground and digging it out. Salt can also be extracted by **solution mining**. A hole is drilled down to the salt deposits and water is pumped down. The salt dissolves to form salt solution. This is pumped to the surface.

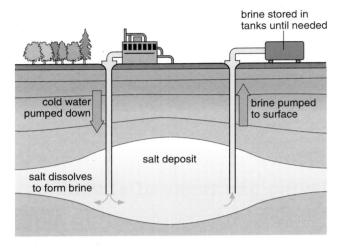

Extracting salt by solution mining.

The salt solution is called **brine** and it is used as a raw material in the chemical industry. Electrolysis of brine is used to produce chlorine, sodium hydroxide and hydrogen. Chlorine is used for sterilising water, by killing micro-organisms in it. The products of the electrolysis are also used in the manufacture of many other products, such as those shown below.

Electrolysis of brine (SS) MM13

Electrolysis of brine (sodium chloride solution) in the laboratory produces chlorine at the positive electrode, and *hydrogen* at the negative electrode rather than sodium as you might expect. Why is this?

Sodium chloride solution contains sodium ions and chloride ions but also some hydrogen and hydroxide ions from water:

$$Na^+ \quad Cl^- \quad H^+ \quad OH^-$$

The chloride ions and the hydroxide ions move towards the positive electrode. Here electrons are transferred to the positive electrode and the chloride ions are discharged to produce chlorine.
The chlorine atoms then combine to form chlorine gas molecules (Cl_2):

$$Cl^- \rightarrow Cl + e^- \qquad 2Cl \rightarrow Cl_2$$

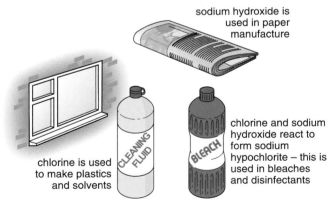

Things made from brine.

The sodium and hydrogen ions move towards the negative electrode. Electrons are transferred from the electrode to the hydrogen ions. The hydrogen atoms then combine to form hydrogen gas molecules (H_2):

$$H^+ + e^- \rightarrow H \qquad 2H \rightarrow H_2$$

The solution becomes a mixture of sodium and hydroxide ions, and so it becomes alkaline as sodium hydroxide builds up.

The cell in the diagram has a porous diaphragm to keep hydrogen and chlorine separate.

Household bleach, which is a dilute solution of sodium chlorate(I) (sodium hypochlorite), NaClO, is made by mixing sodium hydroxide and chlorine:

$$NaOH + Cl_2 \rightarrow NaClO + HCl$$

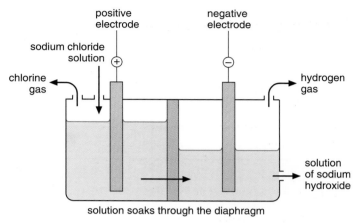

Cell used for the electrolysis of brine in industry.

Purifying copper

For some uses it is important that copper is very pure. For example, for electrical wiring pure copper is much better because impurities increase the resistance.

Impure copper is purified by electrolysis.

In the cell, the positive electrode (anode) is impure copper and the negative electrode (cathode) is pure copper. The electrolyte is copper(II) sulphate solution.

The electrolyte contains:

$$Cu^{2+} \qquad SO_4^{2-} \qquad H^+ \qquad OH^-$$

At the positive electrode, copper from the electrode goes into solution as copper ions:

$$Cu \rightarrow Cu^{2+} + 2e^-$$

At the negative electrode, copper ions are discharged and pure copper metal is deposited.

$$Cu^{2+} + 2e^- \rightarrow Cu$$

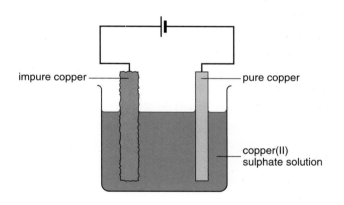

Purification of copper by electrolysis.

Things to do

1. Hydrogen and chlorine from the electrolysis of brine can be combined to form hydrogen chloride.
   a. Write a word equation for this reaction.
   b. Write a balanced symbol equation for the reaction.
2. a. If you electrolysed potassium bromide solution, what would you expect the product at each electrode to be?
   b. Write ionic half-equations for the formation of each of these products.

1   The table gives some information about the extraction of four metals from their ores.

Metal	Formula of main ore	Method of extraction
aluminium	Al_2O_3	electrolysis
copper	Cu_2S	roasting the ore in air
iron	Fe_2O_3	heating with carbon
sodium	NaCl	electrolysis

a   Put the four metals in order of reactivity. Put the most reactive metal first.

b   Write down the name of another metal produced by electrolysis.

c   Explain why aluminium is more expensive than iron although both ores are commonly found in the Earth.

2   This question is about getting tin from tinstone (tin oxide) by heating it with carbon.

tin oxide + carbon → tin + carbon monoxide

$$SnO_2 + 2C \rightarrow Sn + 2CO$$

a   Explain what is happening in the reaction using ideas of oxidation and reduction.

b   What are the relative formula masses of tin oxide, carbon and tin in the equation? (Sn = 119, C = 12, O = 16)

c   Write out and complete the following statement:
From the relative formula masses of tin oxide and tin, 151 tonnes of tin oxide will give _____ tonnes of tin.

d   How much tin can be obtained from 1 tonne of tin oxide?

3   The sulphur dioxide made by roasting lead or zinc sulphide ores is often used to make sulphuric acid.
sulphur dioxide + oxygen → sulphur trioxide
sulphur trioxide + water → sulphuric acid

a   Copy out the word equations above. Write the formula for each substance under its name. (Remember that oxygen is O_2).

b   Add numbers in front of the formulas to **balance** the equations.

c   Calculate the relative formula masses of the substances in your balanced equations (H = 1, S = 32, O = 16)

d   Write out and complete the following statement:
From the relative masses of sulphur and sulphuric acid, _____ tonnes of sulphuric acid can be produced from 32 tonnes of sulphur.

e   How much sulphuric acid can be produced from 16 tonnes of sulphur dioxide?

4   This question is about the extraction of aluminium. It is made form bauxite (impure aluminium oxide).

a   the formula of aluminium oxide is Al_2O_3 (Al = 27, O = 16).
What is the relative formula mass of aluminium oxide?

b   Write out and complete the following statement
From the relative formula mass of Al_2O_3
_____ g of Al_2O_3 contains _____ g of aluminium and _____ g of oxygen.

c   What fraction of the mass of aluminium oxide is aluminium?

d   What percentage of the mass of aluminium oxide is aluminium?

5   The ore calamine contains zinc carbonate. Zinc can be extracted from calamine by two methods.

A   Decompose zinc carbonate by heating. Then heat a mixture of zinc oxide and carbon.

B   Convert zinc carbonate into zinc sulphate solution followed by electrolysis of zinc sulphate solution.

a   Write a detailed account of each method including as many relevant equations as possible.

b   What are the advantages and disadvantages of each method?

6   How much iron can be obtained from 80 tonnes of iron ore (Fe_2O_3)
(Fe = 656, O = 16)

7   What is the percentage of sodium in pure salt (sodium chloride NaCl)?
(Na = 23, Cl = 35.5)

INTRODUCING
Balancing acts

forest in Rwanda, central Africa.

Rainforest in Brazil being cleared to build a road.

Try these first

Look at this food chain.

grass → rabbit → fox

a What is eaten by the rabbit?

b Which organism is a predator?

c What source of energy does the grass use
 to grow?

 fertiliser   the Sun   water

Here are some facts about three animals, A, B
and C.

Animal A has thick fur and small ears.

Animal B has very large ears and smooth skin.

Animal C has very strong claws on its feet.

a Which animal do you think lives in a hot
 desert?

b Which animal lives in the Arctic?

c Which animal lives in a burrow underground?

In this unit you will learn:

● how people and human activities can change the
 environment

● how organisms in an environment live in balance

● how changes in the environment can upset the
 balance of organisms

● how we can protect the environment

● how we can manage the environment to make it
 highly productive, so it can feed us.

Change all around you

How long have you lived where you do now? Has your area changed much in that time?

Everything around you makes up your **environment**. Any environment is made up of living and non-living things. All the parts are delicately balanced with one another. Human activity can change the environment. New homes, new roads, factories and out-of-town shopping centres affect the countryside. Development plans affect the towns.

Upsetting the neighbours

Changes that we make affect the plants and animals that share our environment. Different species have different needs for food, warmth and shelter. For example, mosquitoes require still or very slow moving water to breed – otherwise the mosquito eggs might be washed away. Otters need faster moving water to provide sufficient fish to eat.

In the countryside, hedgerows are often cut down to enlarge fields, to make harvesting easier. This removes food sources and nesting sites. It also removes cover for animals, which are camouflaged by the hedgerow. Fewer small animals and birds mean that kestrels and foxes move away to hunt elsewhere.

Human activities always affect the environment.

Change in the Salt Valley

The maps opposite show part of the Salt Valley, first in the year 1966, then in 2000. In 1966, a stream ran quickly downhill between mixed woods, then spread out onto flat land that was very marshy. A survey counted the numbers of plants and animals living in these areas.

Some years later, a new road was built. A dam was built across the stream. The old trees were cut down and bushes cleared to plant conifer trees, which grow quickly, to supply timber.

The dam helped to control the flow of water down the stream, so that it could be diverted and the marsh could be drained to build new houses as the town grew larger.

Many foxes find the towns a better place to live than the countryside these days.

Another survey of plants and animals was carried out in 2000.

Salt Valley, Summer 1966

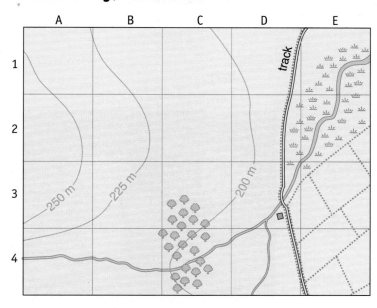

Map of the Salt Valley, 1966.

Results of biological survey		
Map area	Type of plant or animal seen	How many
B3, B4, C3 and C4	badger	few
	otter	few
	red squirrel	few
	nightingale	many
	mosquito	none
	water lily	none
D1, D2, E1 and E2	marsh warbler	few
	marsh marigold	many
	bog orchid	many
	brambles	many
	rat	none
	mouse	none
	marsh fritillary	many
	brown hairstreak	many
	bee	many
	wasp	many

Salt Valley, Summer 2000

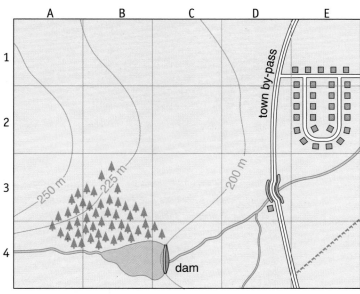

Map of the Salt Valley, 2000.

Key

- marsh
- woodland
- conifer plantation
- hedge
- fence
- house
- stream
- contour line

Results of biological survey		
Map area	Type of plant or animal seen	How many
B3, B4, C3 and C4	badger	none
	otter	none
	red squirrel	none
	nightingale	few
	mosquito	many
	water lily	many
D1, D2, E1 and E2	marsh warbler	none
	marsh marigold	none
	bog orchid	none
	brambles	none
	rat	few
	mouse	few
	marsh fritillary	none
	brown hairstreak	few
	bee	few
	wasp	few

? Things to do

1. Between 1966 and 2000, there have been changes to the numbers of plants and animals in the Salt Valley. Discuss what has caused each of these changes.

Why is biodiversity important?

Biodiversity means having many different kinds of plants and animals around. In many areas, this diversity is getting less, because our actions change or destroy **habitats** (places where particular species can live).

All living organisms are interdependent; animals depend on plants for food, while many plants, in turn, need animals – for seed dispersal, for example. The disappearance of one species has an effect in the ecosystem as a whole, and may lead to loss of other species in the **food web**.

A study of living species aids our understanding of the world around us. Many plants and animals are important sources of useful products. They supply drugs, food, fuels, clothing and building materials – it is not just crop plants that are important. Many ancient civilisations used chemicals extracted from living things, for healing. Drug companies are now finding important new drugs from natural sources. For example, compounds extracted from the rosy periwinkle have been shown to increase recovery rates for childhood leukaemia from 20% to 80%.

It is likely that other products are waiting to be discovered from previously untapped sources. If these species were allowed to disappear, a potential resource would be lost forever.

Many species of plants and animals have become extinct throughout the history of life on this planet, but never at the rate occurring now.

On average, one new species of mammal, three bird species and 100 plants are discovered every year, but many more become extinct in that time.

Some organisms may be essential for evolutionary processes in the future. Gene pools for alternative crops, for example, may be vital if climatic changes alter the world.

The diversity of plants and animals also has important leisure and recreational advantages. Millions of people derive great pleasure from their contact with nature and their need to re-establish this contact grows with increasing industrialisation and prosperity.

The rosy periwinkle produces compounds that can be used to treat childhood leukaemia.

The woolly mammoth became extinct centuries ago, but many more species die out every year these days because of human impact on them and their habitats.

Planning a development BA1

People who live in towns need open spaces for recreation. If care is not taken, this can lead to conflict in the use of land around towns. Many people may be affected, and all of them should be allowed to express their opinions. As part of the planning process for new developments, the public are consulted, and sometimes planning enquiries are held, where each interested group can argue its case.

Making use of what is there

The river area and old canal near Newtown have been allowed to become run down and very overgrown. The canal, which branches off the river and runs into the town, is an eyesore, full of rubbish. The locks are broken and this has let the water level fall so that boats cannot use the river near the town or the canal. There is no proper access to the river bank.

The people who own the land on either side of the river have joined with the council leisure committee to draw up plans for leisure facilities along the banks of the river.

This run down river area near to Newtown seems an ideal site to develop for leisure activities.

The development plan

- Mend the locks, and clear the river. Boats could then sail right into town, using the old canal.
- Restore the old mill and turn it into a working museum.
- Restore the pathway along the river to give country walks and access for pedestrians.
- Improve roads and build car parks for visitors.
- Repair the landing stage and build a boat-house to encourage boat owners and allow river trips.
- Build a footbridge across the river to link all these.

The development could certainly benefit many people – but could it affect some things in an adverse way?

? Things to do

1   Use an encyclopaedia or other source to find out about the Dodo. Write some notes to explain how the Dodo came to be extinct.

2   Why is it that animals that are threatened by a new development can't simply move somewhere else?

3   Think carefully about who would be affected by the changes to the river and canal near Newtown. Also discuss how each change might affect wildlife in the area.

What is an ecosystem?

The word 'environment' is often used in a general sense. A more precise term for the organisms and non-living factors in an area is an ecosystem. The organisms in an **ecosystem** can be grouped into four types.

1 Producers are green plants. They transfer some of the energy in sunlight into food – they store it as chemical energy. They *produce* the food for the rest of the ecosystem. Therefore, the Sun is the source of energy to support all life.

2 Primary consumers are **herbivores**. These are animals that feed on plants and so consume the food the plants have produced.

3 Secondary consumers are **carnivores**. These are animals that feed on other animals. They are **predators** and the animals they eat are their **prey**.

4 Decomposers are organisms that obtain their energy by breaking down the remains of dead animals and plants. They are a very important part of the ecosystem as they help to recycle essential chemicals.

Trees are producers – they produce food using sunlight.

This caterpillar is a primary consumer – it eats green plants.

This nightingale is a secondary consumer – it eats the caterpillar that eats green plants.

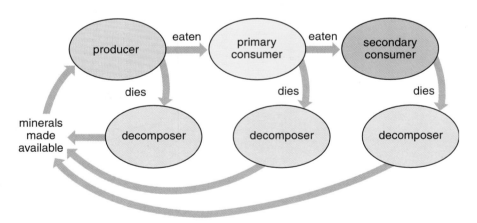

The organisms in an ecosystem interact in a cyclic way.

This fungus is a decomposer – it feeds on dead organisms.

Food chains and webs (SS) BA4

The feeding relationships within an ecosystem can be shown as simple **food chains**. Each chain begins with a producer, which is followed by one or more consumers.

Each consumer eats the species below in the food chain. An arrow is drawn to show the movement of energy from one organism to the next. The arrows always point to the eater!

Food webs show how the different food chains in an ecosystem are linked together. They give a more complete picture than simple food chains. The level at which an organism feeds is called its **trophic level**. If you eat a meat salad you are feeding at two different trophic levels. This can't be shown on a single food chain, but it is possible to show it on a food web.

This is a simple food chain: rabbits eat grass, and foxes eat rabbits.

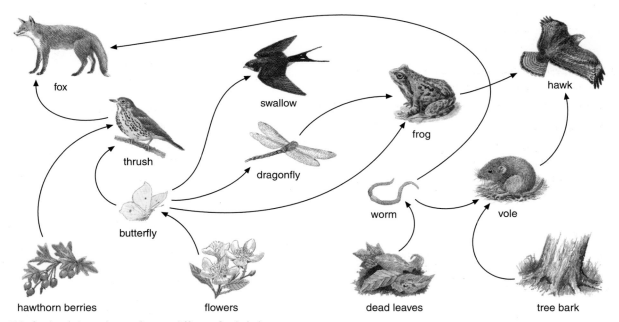

This food web is made up of many different food chains.

? Things to do

1 Write down five different food chains within the food web on this page.

2 Write down all the producers in this food web.

3 Name one organism that is feeding at two different trophic levels.

If the conditions in the ecosystem change, some of the animals may be forced to change their feeding habits. The food web helps you to predict how any change might affect the ecosystem. For example, before the hawthorn berries are ripe, the thrush would have to eat more butterflies to survive.

4 What effect will it have if a disease kills most of the voles?

5 What effect will it have if there is more fox hunting by humans?

6 What effect will it have if farmers in the area remove more of the hedgerows?

7 In the winter there are very few flowers. How do the butterflies survive?

8 What is the source of energy for this food web?

4 How many greenfly make a sparrow?

Pyramids of numbers

Food chains and webs show which species feed on other species. They do not give any idea of *how many* of each species might be present in a population. In a real ecosystem, numbers are important, because a change in the numbers of one species will affect all the other species that depend on it for food. A **pyramid of numbers** is a way of drawing a food chain so that it shows the relative numbers of each species.

As an example, the picture shows a rose bush. Greenfly feed on the bush, ladybirds eat the greenfly, and a sparrow eats the ladybirds. The diagrams show this food chain, and the pyramid of numbers involved.

The sparrow consumes ladybirds, which eat greenfly, which feed on the rose bush.

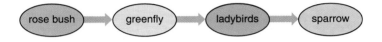

The rose bush–sparrow food chain.

Each trophic level is represented by a box in a pyramid of numbers. Each box is the same height. The width of the box shows the relative numbers of organisms at that level.

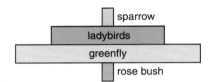

The pyramid of numbers for the rose bush–sparrow food chain.

Pyramids of biomass

Another way of representing food chains is based on the amount of living material (**biomass**) at each trophic level. This means you need to know the mass of each organism as well as the numbers. A **pyramid of biomass** takes into account the different sizes of organisms. Each layer represents the dry weight of the organisms in the food chain at that trophic level. Dry mass is far more difficult to work out – instead of just counting organisms, you have to collect them, dry them (which means killing them) and then measure their mass using scales.

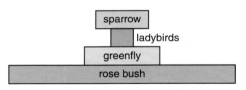

The pyramid of biomass for the rose bush–sparrow food chain

?

Things to do

Draw pyramids of numbers and of biomass for each of the food chains below. (You can't always use an exact scale – just indicate the *relative* sizes of each box.)

1 a 20 cabbages in a garden have a mass of 700 g each. 200 caterpillars (0.2 g each) feed on the cabbages. A thrush (mass 60 g) eats the caterpillars.

   b An African wildebeest has 100 ticks living on it. One ox-pecker bird feeds on the ticks.

Energy flow along a food chain (SS) BA7

All processes that make new biomass take in energy. Green plants get their energy from the Sun for photosynthesis. The chemicals produced are passed along the food chain as proteins, carbohydrates and lipids.

Animals are consumers – they get the energy they need from biomass already made by plants or other animals they eat. At each trophic level of the food chain, energy is lost. Only a few percent is available to be passed on to the next level.

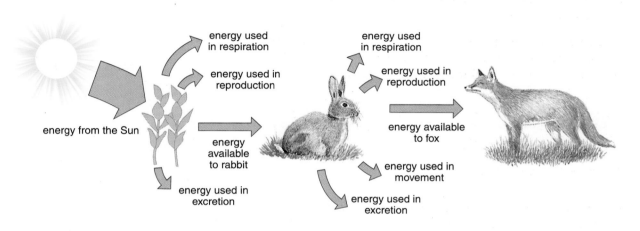

The amount of energy available as food decreases at each stage.

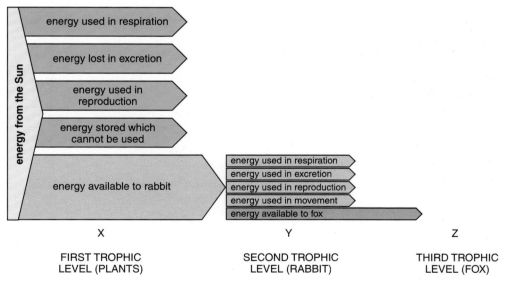

This energy diagram shows what happens to the energy at each trophic level in the food chain.

Population growth

Populations in established ecosystems are stable. They are not getting bigger or smaller. Things are different for a species in a new environment. If a few individuals of a new species are introduced, the change in population over time often looks like this.

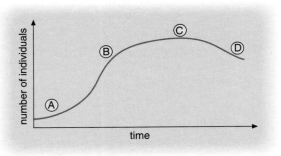

The graph shows four stages in the development of the population.

A Lag phase. The individuals need to become accustomed to the new conditions, and grow before they are mature enough to reproduce.

B Growth phase. More and more individuals are produced to take advantage of the space available.

C Stationary phase. The population becomes stable. The numbers dying or being eaten by predators equals the numbers born. Unless the ecosystem changes, the population has reached its limit.

D Decline or **extinction**. If the resources to support the population become exhausted, or conditions change, the population may begin to decline. Many species become extinct because changes in their environment destroy the conditions they needed to live.

Predator–prey relationships

 BA8

Each species in an environment forms part of the food web for the environment. In some cases, one species is the main **prey** (food) for one particular **predator**.

Because the predator depends on the prey, its population numbers follow those of the prey. A predator–prey relationship often follows the regular pattern described below.

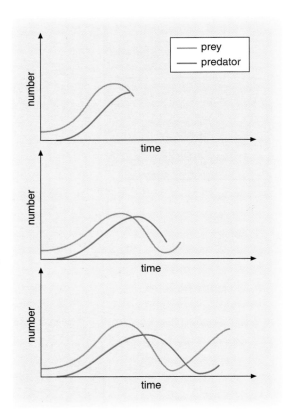

1 Prey increase in number. The predators are well fed and reproduce.

2 With a greater number of predators, more of the prey are eaten, so their numbers start to fall.

3 Fewer prey means less food for the predators, so some starve.

4 Fewer predators to eat the prey means that the prey can now start to increase in number again.

5 And so the cycle goes on.

The size of the predator population follows that of the prey population.

Seasonal changes

Where there is sufficient food and space, species may go on with steady numbers for a long time, unless things change.

Both the temperature and the amount of food available change between winter and summer. In winter many small birds may die from cold or lack of food. In the spring, more insects and other food are available. Birds that have survived the winter begin to breed.

Water pollution (SS) BA10–13

All living things affect the environment in which they live. Life processes such as respiration, feeding and excretion alter the levels of chemicals in the air, water and ground. Usually these substances pass into natural chemical pathways, where decomposers break them down for re-use.

Seasons affect the numbers in a population.

Human activity is also capable of altering the environment. Substances released into the environment through human activity enter chemical pathways and natural cycles, which break them down or absorb them.

Plants that live in water obtain their nutrients from substances that are dissolved in the water. Human activities can greatly increase the amounts of phosphates and nitrates in the water. These substances can have a great effect on species living in lakes, streams or rivers.

Human activities can drastically affect the environment, and therefore affect the populations of organisms living there.

? Things to do

1   Copy out and complete the graph on the right to show how the population of birds changes with the seasons over four years.

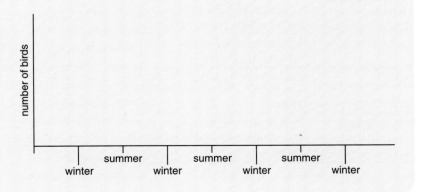

Eutrophication

On land, all food chains start from plants. In water, food chains may start from plants such as pondweed, or from tiny plant-like **algae**. As for plants, the growth of algae can be greatly affected by nutrient levels.

In recent years, increases in levels of nitrates and phosphates in rivers, ponds and lakes have led to the death of many freshwater plants and animals.

Water with very little pollution looks clear. Algae can only be seen if the water is examined using a microscope. The bed of the waterway is free from rotting plant material. Water with higher levels of nitrates and phosphates is often a deep green colour with a blanket of algae covering the surface. Dead plant material is rotting on the waterway bed and the whole area appears lifeless and smelly.

Assessing water quality

Good, pure water has a lot of oxygen dissolved in it and can support a wide range of different animals. If the water is polluted, and especially if it contains little dissolved oxygen, fewer types of animals can live there.

F The sequence of changes leading to this situation is called **eutrophication**:

- Rain washes fertilisers off the land, and drains carry water from houses into streams. Both of these may contain phosphates and nitrates.
- Nitrates and phosphates act as nutrients and cause algae to grow and multiply more quickly.
- Algae are in such large numbers that they form a layer on the surface of the waterway. This prevents light from reaching plants near the bottom, so they die.
- Bacteria decompose the dead plant material. This uses up dissolved oxygen from the water.
- Low levels of oxygen in the water mean that fish and other animals die of suffocation.

Chemical indicators of water quality

Chemical	What affects the amount?
dissolved oxygen	increased by weirs or waterfalls or by access of light to plants decreased by eutrophication
carbon dioxide	high when there is much dead material to decay
nitrates	high levels suggest pollution and may produce excessive growth of algae
phosphates	high levels suggest pollution and may produce excessive growth of algae

Biological indicators of water quality

Water quality	Animals that can live there
Level 4	only sludge worms and rat-tailed maggots
Level 3	sludge worms, rat-tailed maggots, water lice, leeches, flatworms, bloodworms
Level 2	sludge worms, rat-tailed maggots, water lice, leeches, flatworms, bloodworms, caddis fly lavae, freshwater shrimps, water beetles, snails
Level 1	sludge worms, rat-tailed maggots, water lice, leeches, flatworms, bloodworms, caddis fly lavae, freshwater shrimps, water beetles, snails, fish, stonefly larvae, mayfly larvae

Water companies regularly check the quality of water in rivers. They measure both chemical and biological indicators of water quality. These surveys help to detect any pollution problems. Surveys of the River Lugg found where a faulty sewer was leaking raw sewage into the river. These graphs show how this sewage pollution had affected the river.

The water company can tell several things have been changed in the river. All of these changes are caused by the raw sewage.

Pollution in the River Lugg

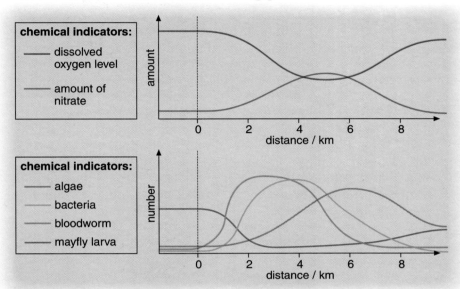

The amounts of each indicator vary with the distance downstream from the source of pollution.

Things to do

1 Why does rotting of dead material in waterways decrease the amount of dissolved oxygen, and increase dissolved carbon dioxide?

2 Look at the graphs and use the information in them to answer the following questions.

  a For each water quality indicator (dissolved oxygen level, number of algae, and so on). Describe how the level or number changes after the sewage enters the river.

  b What processes are using up dissolved oxygen when there is sewage present in the water?

  c Explain why the level of nitrates in the water rises soon after the sewage enters the river.

  d Which of the different species is:

    i least tolerant of low levels of dissolved oxygen

    ii most tolerant of low levels of dissolved oxygen?

  e At what distance downstream does the level of dissolved oxygen begin to recover again?

  f What do you think is likely to happen to the water quality in this part of the river after the leaky sewage pipe has been mended?

Managing food production

Farms are examples of **managed ecosystems**, where conditions are carefully controlled to favour particular species (farm animals or food crops).

Increasing use of machinery means that fewer people work on the land.

Chemicals are also used to help produce more foods. The unit *Food for thought* describes how **fertilisers** can help to increase crop yields.

Insects that attack plants can be controlled by careful crop management or by use of chemicals (**pesticides**). Pesticides are often **non-selective**. They don't just kill pests, but also useful species such as bees, which pollinate crops, or ladybirds, which are predators of a lot of pest species.

Herbicides can be used to control weeds. Weeds compete with crop plants for light and nutrients and reduce the crop. Weeds may be difficult to separate from crop plants at harvesting time, and weeds in a crop may reduce its value.

Many herbicides kill plants that are vital parts of hedgerow food chains. This may force animals from the hedgerows to eat crop plants or face starvation.

Traditional farming methods needed many workers.

Vast areas of farmland can be treated efficiently by spraying chemicals from planes.

Problems with farm chemicals

- Farm chemicals are expensive.
- They are often harmful to pets and other animals if not used carefully.
- Some remain in or on the crop and so may end up in our food.
- **Persistent** pesticides may enter food chains. For example, a chemical called DDT, applied to kill mosquitoes in tropical countries, has been detected in penguins in the Antarctic.

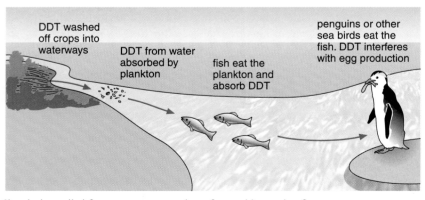

DDT washed off crops into waterways

DDT from water absorbed by plankton

fish eat the plankton and absorb DDT

penguins or other sea birds eat the fish. DDT interferes with egg production

Chemicals applied for one purpose can have far-reaching and unforeseen consequences.

Farming past and present

This table shows some of the changes in farming over the years.

	Past	Present
Machinery	Work was by hand. Many labourers were needed, work was hard and slow and could only be done in daylight. Horses did heavy work like ploughing.	Most jobs are now done by machine. Fewer labourers are needed. Tractors have replaced horses. Fields have been made larger.
Use of chemicals	Recycled waste such as manure was used as fertiliser. This helped to improve soil structure and drainage. Crops were rotated to maintain fertility and avoid build-up diseases or pests in the soil.	Artificial fertiliser is used to give larger crops. If care is not taken, some may be washed into streams. Pesticides and herbicides reduce loss of crops, but may affect wild plants and animals.
Hedges and trees	Farms were often small. Fields were small and separated by hedges. Trees grew in the hedges and hand cultivation often left bushes and shrubs round fields as extra shelter for birds, animals and flowers.	Fields are larger to save time moving machines. Many hedges and trees have been removed. Fields are cultivated right to the edges. Soil may be eroded because there are few trees to break the wind.

Until a few hundred years ago, most people worked on the land. Now a few people can produce large amounts of food and most people live in towns.

Whole new industries have grown up transporting and distributing food. Food technologists have devised ways to preserve food until it reaches the shops.

? Things to do

1   Make a list of the changes that have taken place in farming. For each one, decide how it may have affected the wild plants and animals living on or around the farms.

Tractors and other highly specialised machines make farming more efficient

The sea as a managed ecosystem

It is not only farm land that can produce food. Seven-tenths of the Earth is covered by water. Seas, lakes and rivers have always provided fish to add to our diet. In commercial fishing, two main types of nets are used, as shown in the drawings.

If not over-exploited, fish are a renewable resource. The fish left in the sea breed to replace those we have taken. Fishing with nets with large holes catches older fish, but lets smaller, younger fish escape. The young fish can then breed to restore the population.

Too much fishing, however, reduces stocks of some fish species. Once **overfishing** starts, it becomes harder to keep up the catch numbers. To keep up their catch, and so their income, fishermen might use nets with a smaller mesh. This means that smaller fish are caught, which leads to a decrease in the breeding efficiency of the population. So the decrease in numbers becomes more and more rapid. International controls to regulate the numbers and sizes of fish caught are in operation, but the area they cover is vast and it is not always easy to enforce the regulations.

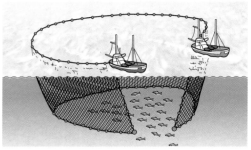

Seine nets are long strips of net that catch fish swimming near to the surface.

Trawl nets are large sack-shaped nets that are towed along the seabed to catch fish living there.

Fish farming

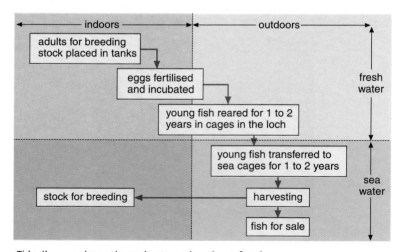

This diagram shows the main stages in salmon farming.

Throughout history there have been many attempts to 'farm' fish. Four thousand years ago, the Chinese reared carp in ponds. The Greeks, Romans and Japanese grew oysters in shallow coastal waters, and British monks raised carp and roach in streams and ponds.

In Britain today, fish that sell for a high price – for example, salmon, trout, sole and turbot – are reared in fish farms.

Salmon are suitable for farming because they grow quickly and fetch a high price. An artificial ecosystem is set up to farm the salmon.

There are four main problems with fish farming.

- Expensive high-protein diets are required to give faster growth. Uneaten food can upset the balance of nutrients in the surrounding body of water.
- To reduce costs, it is necessary to keep a large number of fish in each cage. When fish are so close together disease is likely to spread rapidly. Good hygiene is needed to prevent disease.
- Salmon kept close together are at risk from a parasite, the sea-louse, which damages the skin of the salmon and may kill them. Controlling the parasite involves either a chemical pesticide or biological control using a fish called the sinny wrasse, which eats the sea-lice.
- It is expensive to keep predators and competitors out of the salmon cages.

? Things to do

1 Discuss the likely costs of setting up a salmon farm.
- What buildings or equipment will be needed?
- What are the costs of keeping the fish?
- How long will it be before the first fish are ready for sale?
- How might the local environment be affected?

2 What are the advantages of farming salmon rather than relying on catching salmon from the sea, rivers or streams?

3 Find a tree growing near to a busy road, and one of the same species growing in a quiet park. Make a list of any differences you can see. Can any of these differences be explained by pollution?

4 This list shows some relationships between living things:
- **A** Sinny wrasse fish keep down parasites on salmon.
- **B** Foxes kill rabbits for food.
- **C** Freshwater plants and animals can be kept in a school aquarium.
- **D** Algae are eaten by small invertebrates, which in turn are eaten by fish.

Choose the letter **A**, **B**, **C** or **D** that shows an example of:

a a predator-prey relationship   b biological control

c an artificial ecosystem   d a food chain.

5 Flowers in a park attract butterflies, but the plants are attacked by slugs. Thrushes come to the park because they eat slugs and butterflies.

a Draw a food web for all these species.

b Identify one producer and one primary consumer in the web.

c If the slugs are killed using slug pellets, how will this affect the numbers of:

i thrushes   ii butterflies?

1   Use some of the words from this list to fill in the gaps in the following paragraph:

fertilisers   **fungicides**   **hormones**
insecticides   **herbicides**
food crops   **species**

Farming activities have changed so that _____ are produced more efficiently. _____ have been added to the land to increase growth of cereals and vegetables. Animals have been treated with _____ to speed up their growth. Plants are sprayed with _____ to remove unwanted insects. One problem, however, is that chemicals remain in the soil and affect other _____ of plants and animals.

2   Ponds or slow moving streams which become polluted with fertilisers washed off nearby fields may suffer from excessive growth of algae.

Describe the stages by which this can lead to eutrophication, and how this would affect fish living in the water.

3   The graph across the foot of this page shows the numbers of different species in a small lake over one year.

a   Name two nutrients which are important for the growth of unicellular algae.

b   The graph shows that the number of unicellular algae increased during the spring. Suggest why this happened.

c   Describe and explain the changes in the population of small water animals at each time of year.

d   Suggest why the concentration of nutrients rose in the autumn.

4   A hundred years ago, grain crops were cut by hand and stacked in the fields. The stacks provided food for rats and mice, and these attracted owls.

a   Construct a food chain for the species mentioned in this question.

b   Explain how modern farming methods have led to a decrease in the numbers of owls.

5   Joy made a small pond in her garden. She put in a few small pondweed plants.

Complete a graph of number of plants against time like this one to show how the pondweed population would develop.

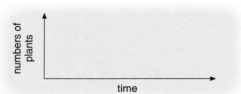

Explain what is happening at each stage on the graph.

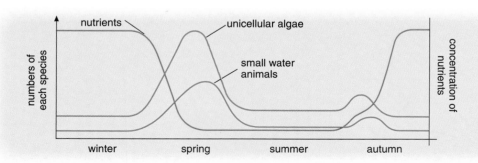

INTRODUCING
Communicating information

Many different kinds of waves are used in communication.

Try these first

A sound with a higher pitch has a _____ frequency.

Light always travels in _____ _____.

Light waves will reflect so that the angle of _____ is equal to the angle of _____.

Light is _____ when it leaves one material and enters another.

Light travels much _____ than sound.

Light can travel through a _____ but sound cannot.

A magnet has _____ and _____ poles.

Like magnetic poles _____ and unlike poles _____.

An electric current in a wire causes a _____ field around the wire.

In this unit you will learn:

- that waves can be reflected, refracted and diffracted
- the meanings of the terms frequency, wavelength and amplitude and how they affect the waves that we see and hear
- about uses of electromagnetism in recording sounds
- about transverse and longitudinal waves
- how lenses make images
- how the eye and the camera work
- about optical fibres and their uses
- about using radio waves, microwaves and satellites for communication
- about digital and analogue signals and their uses in recordings.

Using your senses CI1

Humans have five senses and we use them to communicate with each other. This section concentrates on the senses that work by receiving waves – sight and hearing.

To pass a message to friends who are nearby, you speak to them: you are using sound waves to carry the information. If your friends are a bit further away, you might wave at them: your signal is carried by light waves. Mobile phones, radio or television systems convert light or sound waves from the sender into radio waves or microwaves, which can travel long distances. A suitable receiver is needed to turn the radio or microwaves back into sound or light waves that we can detect.

Mobile phone systems use microwaves to help you communicate over long distances.

What are sound waves? SS CI2

You have probably studied sound and know that sound waves need vibrating particles to carry them.

All sound starts at something that is vibrating. Air is pushed together to start the vibrations, which travel through the air to reach our ears. Sound needs a medium, such as air, to carry it. It cannot travel through a vacuum.

Sound is an example of a **longitudinal wave** – the particles vibrate backwards and forwards in the same direction as that in which the wave is travelling. The result is that the particles are alternately squashed together and then spread out, so that a series of **compressions** travel outwards. You can see another example of this if you stretch a slinky spring along a desk and then pull some of the coils together.

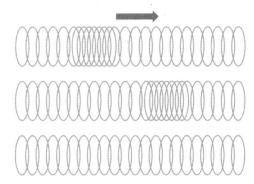

The spring is being pushed and pulled, making a longitudinal wave as each spring vibrates back and forth.

Light waves are different

Most other waves, including light, are **transverse waves**. In these waves the vibration is at right angles to the direction of travel.

You can demonstrate transverse waves with a slinky too, or with a rope. Stretch it out and move the end from side to side so that the sideways waves travel along.

You can see transverse waves quite clearly when ripples travel across a water surface.

Waves transmit energy

A water surface goes up and down as ripples move across it. A float will bob up and down as the wave passes, but the float isn't carried along.

In each of these types of wave the particles that are vibrating do *not* travel along with the wave. If you throw a stone into a pond the ripples travel outwards but they don't take the water with them leaving a hole in the middle of the pond! What is carried along by the wave is *energy*, which is transferred from one place to another.

Describing waves

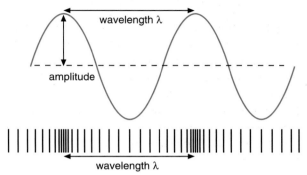

Wavelength is the length of one complete wave. It is usually given the symbol λ (lamda).

Some waves are very short – X-rays have a wavelength of about 0.000 000 000 1 m. Some waves are very long – some radio waves are 1500 m in wavelength.

Frequency (f) is the number of waves per second. One wave per second is called a hertz (1 Hz). A radio station that sends out a signal at 100 MHz is sending out 100 000 000 waves per second!

Three features can be used to describe waves – wavelength, frequency and amplitude.

Amplitude (a) is the greatest distance that a particle moves on each side of its rest position. A wave with bigger amplitude has a bigger vibration and is carrying more energy – brighter light or louder sound.

How fast do waves go?

If you stand on a harbour wall, watching waves go by, you can count how many go past in each second (in other words, the frequency of the waves).

If you multiply the number of waves that pass by the length of each one (wavelength), you can tell how far the waves travel in each second.

F

> wavespeed (m/s) = frequency (Hz) × wavelength (m)
>
> This is called the **wave equation**. It can be used for any type of wave, to tell how fast the wave is travelling.

?

Things to do

1   Name the five senses. Explain how each one might be used to convey a message.

2   Find out what system was set up to warn of the approach of the Spanish Armada. Why was it necessary to have signals only a few miles apart?

3   See if you can find out the frequency that your mobile phone uses to transmit its signal.

4   Explain the difference between longitudinal and transverse waves. Give an example of each.

6   The musical note 'middle C' has frequency 262 Hz and the wavelength in air is 1.3 m. What is the speed of sound in air?

2 Getting sound taped

How can you store sound?

Sound waves fade away quickly and it isn't possible to store them. However, you can keep a record of what the waves were like.

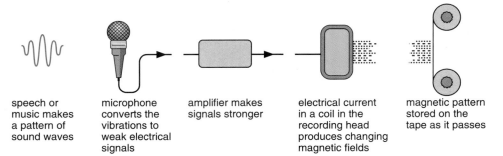

speech or music makes a pattern of sound waves

microphone converts the vibrations to weak electrical signals

amplifier makes signals stronger

electrical current in a coil in the recording head produces changing magnetic fields

magnetic pattern stored on the tape as it passes

This diagram shows the stages in making a tape recording of sound.

Some reminders about magnets

Iron, steel and a few other metals (for example, nickel) can be **magnetised**. When a magnetic field affects the metal, tiny clusters of atoms, called domains, line up in the direction of the field. Each domain acts like a tiny magnet, so as they line up, the whole piece of metal becomes magnetised.

If you hang a bar of magnetised iron or steel so that it can swing, it will settle pointing north–south. The end that points north is called the north-seeking pole (or north pole, for short). The other end is the south pole.

unmagnetised

magnetised

When an iron bar is magnetised, all its domains are aligned in the same direction.

F All magnets have north and south poles. Like poles repel (push apart) and opposite poles attract each other.

Magnetic fields

The effect of a magnet spreads out around it. This effect is called a **magnetic field**. Magnets attract iron or steel objects.

Recording tape

Tape in a tape-recorder is a strip of plastic, coated with an easily-magnetised material. A magnetic pattern is stored on the tape and represents the original pattern of sound.

? Things to do

1 Draw a bar magnet. Label the poles, and draw lines to show the magnetic field round the magnet.

2 Which of these would be attracted to a magnet?
   a brick   b copper wire   c iron nail
   d paper   e steel paper-clip   f diamond

3 How could you use a bar magnet to test a strip of steel to see whether it was magnetised or not?

Playing the sound back again

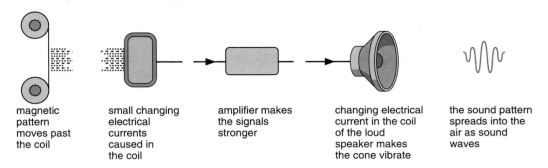

| magnetic pattern moves past the coil | small changing electrical currents caused in the coil | amplifier makes the signals stronger | changing electrical current in the coil of the loud speaker makes the cone vibrate | the sound pattern spreads into the air as sound waves |

Playing back the sound from a tape recording is almost the reverse of the stages in recording it.

Electromagnetism (SS) CI4

If a wire carrying an electric current is near a compass, the needle changes direction. An electric current causes a magnetic field around it.

If the wire is coiled to form a **solenoid**, the magnetic effects from all the turns add up to form a strong field.

A piece of iron or steel put inside the coil (a **core**) becomes magnetised when the current is on. This type of arrangement is called an electromagnet. One advantage of **electromagnets** is that they can be turned on or off, or varied in strength, by changing the electric current.

The recording head is an electromagnet

When you record a sound, small electrical signals from the microphone are made bigger by the amplifier. The current gets larger and smaller in step with the vibrations of the sound waves. This current goes through an electromagnet. The strength of the electromagnet varies in step with changes in the current.

As the tape passes, the field from the electromagnet magnetises the coating of the tape. The magnetic pattern varies in step with the field. Thus, at each stage, the original pattern of the sound waves is copied.

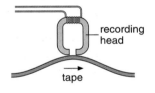

As the magnetic tape passes the recording head, the original pattern of the sound wave creates a corresponding magnetic pattern in the tape coating.

? Things to do

4 Draw a solenoid and draw lines round it to show the magnetic field.

5 How would each of these changes affect the strength of the electromagnet?

   a adding more turns to the coil   b increasing the electric current

6 A device that transfers energy is called a **transducer**. Decide which of the parts of a tape recorder are transducers. For each one, decide the form of energy that makes it work, and the form of energy that it produces.

Loudspeakers (SS) CI6

Devices like radios, televisions, tape-recorders or telephones produce electric currents that get bigger and smaller in the same pattern as the sound waves originally spoken or played in.

If the electric current is passed through a coil of wire, it causes a magnetic field, which also varies in the same pattern. This is the basis for loudspeakers.

The coil is fixed to a flexible cone. When a current flows through the coil, the magnetic field that is caused pulls the cone towards a permanent magnet fixed inside the casing behind the cone.

As the current varies, the cone is moved backwards and forwards, sending out pressure waves into the air in front. The pattern of these sound waves matches the variations in the current.

In this way, the original sound signal is recreated.

For you to hear sound that was originally recorded or transmitted, the varying electric current must be converted to sound waves in the air.

Why use more than one speaker?

As a general rule, the larger a loudspeaker is, the louder the sound it can make. You might wonder why many sound systems have a small speaker as well as a larger one.

When sound waves pass through an opening (like the cone of a loudspeaker) they are spread out, or **diffracted**. This is just like the spreading of water waves as they pass an obstruction.

Diffraction is what lets you hear sound even though you are not straight in front of the speaker. The greater the diffraction, the more widely and evenly the sound is spread.

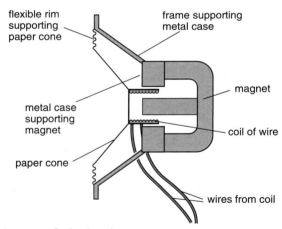

flexible rim supporting paper cone

frame supporting metal case

metal case supporting magnet

magnet

coil of wire

paper cone

wires from coil

Structure of a loudspeaker.

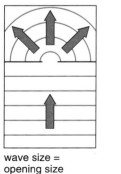

wave size = opening size

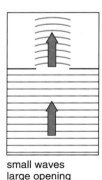

small waves large opening

Waves are diffracted as they pass through an opening.

Diffraction is at its greatest when the opening is no larger than the wavelength of the sound. High pitched notes, near the upper frequency limit we can hear, have wavelengths of just a few centimetres. Large speakers do not diffract these waves well – the sound only travels forwards.

Many sound systems have a large speaker to give good reproduction of low notes (longer wavelengths), and a small speaker to spread the high notes more widely.

The 'woofer' cone produces lower notes, while the smaller 'tweeter' cone is responsible for higher-pitched sounds.

Things to do

1 Andrew and Sarah are investigating waves. They use a rope to see how waves travel.

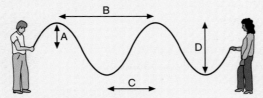

Which of the distances **A**, **B**, **C** or **D** shows:

a the wavelength

b the amplitude?

2 Explain the differences between transverse waves and longitudinal waves.

3 A signal generator produces waves with frequency 500 Hz. The wavelength of the waves is 0.66 metres.

a What is the speed of sound?

b if the generator now makes waves of frequency 1320 Hz, what will their wavelength be?

4 In an electrical storm, the thunder that you hear is the noise made by lightning that you see.

a Explain why you see the lightning before you hear the thunder.

b Sarah sees a lightning flash. Six seconds later, she hears the thunder. If the speed of sound in air is 330 m/s, how far away is the storm?

5 These electromagnets are attracting one another.

Discuss how the force between them would be altered by each of the changes listed below. Consider just the effect of that change only from what is shown in the diagram.

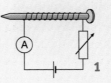 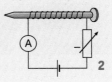

a Increase the current in circuit 1 only.

b Unwind some of the wire from the coils to decrease the number of turns.

c Reverse the current in circuit 1 only.

d Reverse the current in both circuits.

6 Jemma is listening to sound coming through a doorway from another room. The sound has a frequency of 680 Hz. The doorway is 0.7 m wide. Explain why Jemma is able to hear the sound wherever she stands in the room.

4 Reflecting on mirrors

Look in the looking glass

A **plane mirror** is a flat mirror like the ones that we often use at home. To help you judge the angle at which light hits a mirror or lens, draw a line at right angles to the surface (this is called a **normal**). You measure the **angle of reflection** from the normal.

 The angle of reflection is equal to the angle of incidence.

You see the reflected light coming towards you. It seems to be coming from behind the mirror. The point the reflected rays seem to be coming from is where you see the image in the mirror. The image is the same distance behind the mirror as the object is in front, along a line that crosses the mirror at 90°.

The image is called a **virtual image**, because the light only *appears* to come from behind the mirror – there isn't actually anything there!

If you find the image positions of several points on an object, you will see that the image is the same size as the object but is turned sideways. This is called **lateral inversion.**

You can make a simple periscope.

How the periscope works.

Some mirrors bulge out

If you look into a curved mirror rather than a plane one then you will see something quite different.

A **convex** mirror will curve out towards you. The back of a spoon will show this if you don't have a special mirror. The image that you get is always smaller than the object and is the right way up. The image is virtual again.

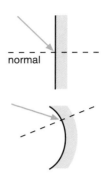

The 'normal' is at right angles to the surface of the mirror.

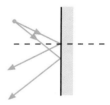

Copy this diagram, and extend the lines of the reflected rays back behind the mirror.

Car mirrors are convex to give a wider view than a flat mirror.

Some mirrors curve in

A concave mirror will change your image too. A concave mirror curves inwards away from you – like the front of the spoon.

If you are close to the mirror and it is not too curved, you get a magnified image that is the right way up. It is a virtual image.

As you move further away the image is inverted (back to front and upside down). Its size depends on how far the object is from the mirror. The light does go to the image and you can focus it onto a screen. It is a **real** image.

All sorts of waves can be reflected

A satellite TV aerial will collect all the radio waves that hit it and reflect them onto the sensor at the focus of the mirror. The waves will probably be quite weak but collecting them over a bigger area like this makes the total signal strong enough.

The same shape of reflector can also be used to send out a beam of radio waves. Microwave repeater stations collect radio waves and microwaves, amplify them and send them on to the next station. Mobile phone messages are transmitted in this way. When you switch on your phone you may see a message 'searching' while it finds the nearest signal.

Shaving mirrors are concave, to give an enlarged image of your face.

Transmitting waves in a clear signal also involves concave dishes.

? Things to do

1   Find out other uses for plane mirrors, convex mirrors and concave mirrors. In each case find out why that particular type of mirror is used. Compare your list with others in your class – who has most?

2   Find out what a kaleidoscope is. Can you borrow some mirrors and make one?

3   Use books or the Internet to find the size of the mirror in the world's largest reflecting telescope. Where is this telescope, and why was it built there?

5 Looking through lenses

Different types of lens

A **lens** is a piece of glass or clear plastic used to direct rays of light. Some lenses are thinner in the middle than at the edges. They are called **concave** lenses.

Light rays passing through a concave lens are spread apart. This sort of lens is also called a **diverging** lens. The image is always smaller than the object, the right way up and virtual.

Lenses that are thickest in the middle are **convex**. They bend light rays towards a focus and are called **converging** lenses.

With a converging lens the type of image you get depends on how far the **object** (the source of light) is away from the lens. Borrow a magnifying glass and look at some writing through it. It only works if the distance between the lens and the paper is less than the **focal length** of the lens.

Light from long distance (SS) CI12

The magnifying glass only works if the object is very close to the lens. You can find out what happens with distant objects using a lamp or ray box with a cross-wire in front of it to act as the object. You also need a lens, a white screen and a metre rule.

If you move the cross-wires further from the lens you find that you have to move the screen closer to the lens to keep the image clear and sharp. The image distance is getting smaller and so is the image itself.

This sort of small image at a small distance from the lens is formed in the camera, and in the eye (see page 177).

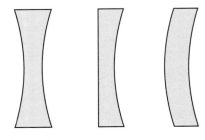
Concave lenses.

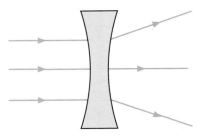
Concave lenses make a parallel beam of light diverge.

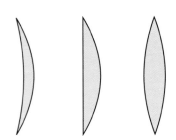
Convex lenses are thicker in the middle than at the edges.

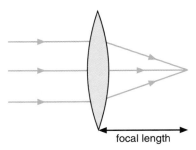
Convex lenses make a parallel beam of light converge, to a focal point.

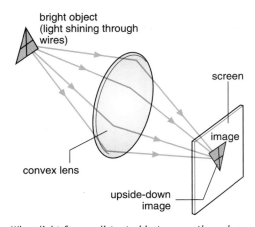
When light from a distant object passes through a convex lens, the image produced is small and inverted.

Capturing the image

The arrangement in a camera is rather like the experiment on the previous page. A converging lens is used to make a small image, just a short distance behind the lens.

Behind the lens is a diaphragm made of metal blades with a hole at the centre called an aperture. This aperture can be made larger so that enough light gets to the film in dull conditions.

The film is behind the shutter, which only opens for a short time to let the correct amount of light through. In many cameras, you can control this time so that you can photograph in bright or dim light, and photograph moving objects without them getting blurred. The exposed film is then wound on so that you use a new piece for each shot.

The image is inverted – but you can always turn your pictures the right way up!

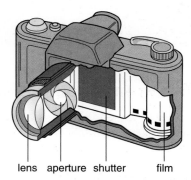

lens aperture shutter   film

The camera is a light-proof box and the lens can be moved backwards and forwards so that you can focus objects at different distances.

Projecting a big image

Film or slide projectors also use a converging lens. The object is the film or the slide, which is brightly lit, and is just slightly more than the focal distance away from the lens.

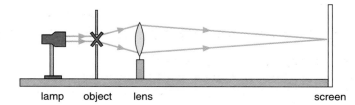

lamp   object   lens   screen

Like the eye and the camera, projectors invert the image, so you have to put the slide or film in upside down.

? Things to do

1. Look at the photograph and complete the following:

   The image is _____ than the object and is the _____ way up. You cannot show the image on a screen as it is a _____ image.

2. In the lens experiment, a magnified image is not as bright as a smaller image. Why is this?

3. Which sort of lens is used in a camera? Describe the image that is made as carefully as you can.

4. Draw a diagram of a camera, labelling the working parts and showing the path of the light as it reaches the image through the lens.

5. Why is the camera made as a light-proof box? Why is the inside painted dull black?

Some facts about light

You will already have studied some facts about light, which are important in explaining how we can see things.

What you should know:

- Light travels in straight lines.

- Some objects are luminous – they give out light. Most of these are hot, like the Sun or a light bulb.

- Most of the things that we see don't give out light but they do reflect it and we see the light that is reflected.

- White light is a mixture of colours that we call a **spectrum**. You can see this using a prism or when light passes through water drops to form a rainbow.

- Coloured objects reflect the coloured light that you can see – a red rose reflects red light and absorbs all the other colours.

How does the eye work? (SS) CI14

You can see because light enters your eye and is focused at the back. Nerves detect the light and send messages to your brain.

Your eye is spherical in shape except for a bulge at the front called the **cornea** where the light enters.

Between the cornea and the lens, the light must get through a hole in the **iris** called the **pupil**. The iris is the coloured part of the eye – it contracts in poor light so that the pupil is larger and more light is let into the eye.

Having gone through the **lens**, the light passes through a thicker liquid, the **vitreous humour**, and reaches the **retina**. The thick liquid acts as a shock absorber to prevent damage.

The retina is covered with millions of special cells that can detect light. When light hits a cell like this it sends a message along the **optic nerve** to the **brain**. Some of these cells, called **rods**, are for seeing in dark conditions, and give 'black and white' vision. The others are called **cones** and detect colour.

The light is *focused* on the retina. This produces an image on the retina that is much smaller than the original object and is inverted (back to front and upside down).

The lens in the eye can focus objects at different distances by changing its shape. The **ciliary muscle** can make the lens fatter and more curved to see close objects, or thinner and less curved for distant objects.

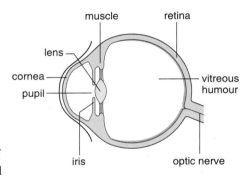

Light enters your eyes through the cornea, pupil and lens, and is focused on the retina.

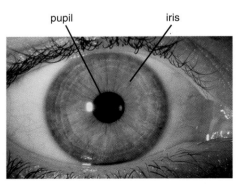

The iris is a muscular ring that controls the size of the pupil.

I can see clearly now

People have used lenses to correct vision for over 600 years.

There are several eyesight problems that can be corrected by spectacles. The two most common are long sight and short sight.

In long sight, either the eyeball is too short, or the lens is not strong enough. The lens needs some help to bend the light rays together more. A converging lens is used in the spectacles.

In short sight, either the eyeball is too long or the lens is too strong. The eye needs another lens of opposite type to bend the rays apart a little. A diverging lens is used in the spectacles.

This picture, painted in 1392, is the earliest to show someone wearing spectacles. They were probably first worn by monks who used to copy manuscripts before the invention of printing.

Comparing the eye with a camera (SS) CI16

There are a number of similarities between your eye and a camera. You can find parts of each that do very similar jobs.

- Both the camera and the eye use a converging lens to make a small, real, inverted image.
- The iris and the diaphragm both have a central hole that can be made bigger in darker light.
- Both the camera and the eye have a light-sensitive surface – the film or the retina.
- Both the camera shutter and the eye-lids can be closed to keep out unwanted light.

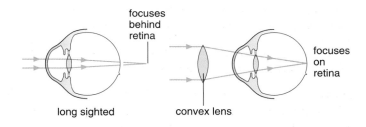

Convex lenses can be used to correct long sight.

There are also some ways in which the eye is different to the camera.

- The eye can change the shape of its lens to focus on different distances but the camera lens has to be moved in and out.
- Camera film can only be used once but the cells on the retina respond over and over again, like the cells in a video camera or digital camera. Cells on the retina can respond about 15 times per second, so that we can keep track of moving objects.

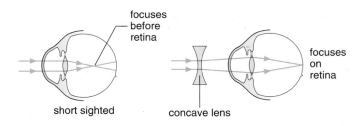

Concave lenses can be used to correct short sight.

Refraction and the speed of light CI17

Light travels at 300 000 000 m/s in a vacuum. In other materials it travels at slower speeds. If the waves hit a boundary between two materials at an angle the speed change causes them to change direction. This is called **refraction**.

Refraction can be seen at the surface of a lens or a glass block or a prism. It also happens when waves pass between air and water.

Refraction can be studied in more detail by looking at what happens when a single ray enters or leaves a glass block. The light bends *towards* the normal as it enters the glass, and *away* from it as it leaves. If it hits the surface at 90° it will travel straight on along the normal without changing direction.

Refraction happens because one edge of the ray slows down before the other edge so that it is turned as it crosses the surface.

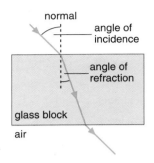

Light is refracted as it passes into a different medium.

Total internal reflection CI19

As light leaves the glass, it is bent away from the normal. If the angle inside the glass is increased, the ray reaches a point where it is *just* escaping along the surface. The angle inside is called the **critical angle**.

If the angle inside is made even bigger, the light reflects back inside. *All* of the light is reflected, so it is actually better than a mirror, which absorbs some of the light. The effect is called **total internal reflection**.

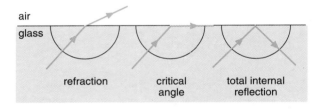

If the angle of incidence is greater than the critical angle, then total internal reflection occurs. None of the light passes out of the straight surface of the block.

Optical fibres CI21

Optical fibres are very fine glass threads. Once light enters one end, it cannot escape because it is totally internally reflected each time it hits the sides. If the fibre is very fine it can be bent without changing the angles enough to let the light out. The light must follow the path of the fibre to the other end.

Optical fibres are replacing copper wires for telephone, computer and cable TV links. They are smaller, lighter and cheaper than copper. The signal is sent by switching the light on and off very rapidly. The light travels down the fibre and is decoded at the other end.

Endoscopes are used to look inside your stomach. Endoscopes are thin flexible tubes made of many optical fibres. Light from a lamp travels down some of the fibres, and is reflected back up the other fibres to show what is inside you.

Radio spreads the word

On page 170, we saw that waves can be diffracted (spread out) as they pass through an opening. Radio waves also diffract when they pass through a gap or round an obstacle.

As with sound, the effect depends on the wavelength. Microwaves and short-wave radio waves do not show much diffraction.

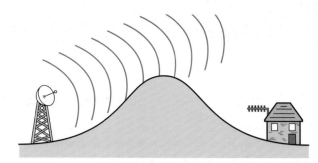

Short waves and microwaves tend to travel in straight lines, and do not bend around obstacles. Many local FM radio stations, therefore, need two or more transmitters to reach all their listeners.

Satellites increase range

Very short radio waves and microwaves tend to go straight through the ionosphere and can't reach places beyond the horizon from their transmitter.

We can get round this if we use satellites in orbit round the Earth. The transmitter sends a signal up to a satellite, which sends it to another satellite, and then the signal is sent back down to Earth. The waves travel in straight lines and their huge speed makes the delay seem small. Microwaves are used so that they don't reflect from the ionosphere.

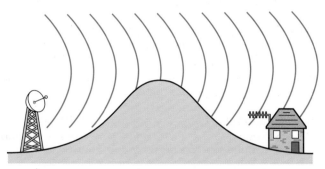

Long-wave radio waves show more diffraction, which means they can reach more listeners.

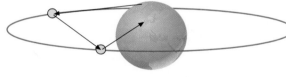

The best orbit for this kind of communication occurs when the satellite seems to be stationary above a particular place. The satellite orbits directly above the equator once every 24 hours (that is, at the same rate as the Earth itself is turning) at about 36 000 km above the surface. There are a number of satellites in 'geostationary orbits' like this, so signals can be sent from one to another to reach the far side of the Earth.

When you use a link like this to phone Australia there is often a gap between you speaking and getting a reply, which is caused by the large distance that the travel waves have to travel, there and back!

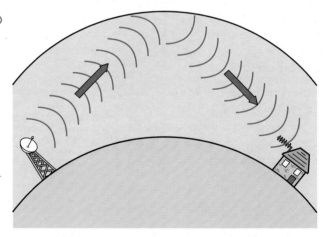

There is a layer of charged particles in the upper atmosphere called the ionosphere. This reflects medium or long-wave radio waves, which can be reflected off it just like using a mirror, so that the signals can reach further.

? Things to do

1   If the distance there and back for a satellite telephone signal is 180 000 km, and the speed of the radio wave is 300 000 km/s, what is the shortest time after which you could get a reply?

2   Grandad used to listen to pop music in Bristol that was transmitted from a radio station in Luxembourg. Write and explain to him how the signal reached him.

8 Digital or analogue?

If you make a copy of music on tape, the copy is not quite as good as the original. But if you make a copy on a CD or DVD, the copy will be just as good as the original!

The difference is that the tape uses **analogue** recording whereas the CD or DVD use **digital** recording. Analogue means that the readings can have any value – like the hands moving round a clock. Digital means readings are represented by numbers and go up or down in small steps – like the numbers on a digital watch.

Digital recording of sound

Digital recordings consist of a series of numbers that represent the sound at a particular instant. The pattern on the CD has only 0s and 1s (the binary number system) but a CD player can quickly recover the numbers from the disc and use them one after another to reproduce the sound in full detail.

If enough numbers can be recorded, there can be enough information for a video or film. This requires the extra space of a DVD rather than a CD.

Digital recording is more 'faithful' than analogue.

Storing music digitally

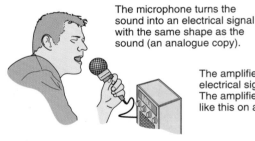

The microphone turns the sound into an electrical signal with the same shape as the sound (an analogue copy).

The amplifier makes the electrical signal bigger. The amplified signal looks like this on a CRO.

The signal is then sampled. Various points along the curve are turned into binary numbers.

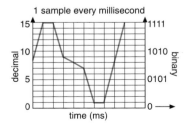

1 sample every millisecond

The more often the samples are taken and the more bits you use for the sampling, the closer the sampled wave is to the original and the better the recording is.

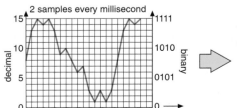

2 samples every millisecond

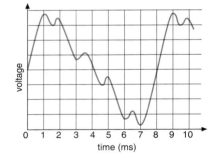

The signal can now be stored as a series of numbers.

In decimal: 08 13 15 14 15
                      13 09 10 08 06...

In binary: 1000 1101 1111 1110 1111
                   1101 1001 1010 1000...

How are the numbers put onto the disc?

After sampling, the music has become a long string of binary numbers – all 0s and 1s. The 0s are small pits etched into the surface of the CD. The 1s are flat, and act like little mirrors.

A CD uses 16-bit numbers so that the sound at an instant is recorded accurately. On a CD the numbers are recorded 44 100 times a second. This is a little more than twice the highest frequency that we can hear so our ears can't detect the difference between this and continuous sound.

The information is recorded on the surface of the CD as a pattern of pits.

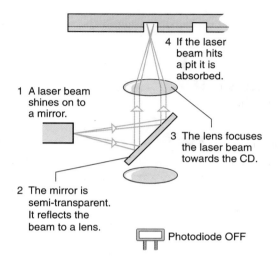

1 A laser beam shines on to a mirror.

2 The mirror is semi-transparent. It reflects the beam to a lens.

3 The lens focuses the laser beam towards the CD.

4 If the laser beam hits a pit it is absorbed.

Photodiode OFF

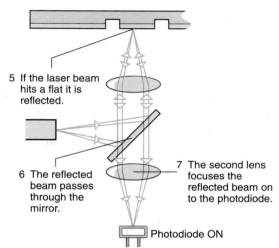

5 If the laser beam hits a flat it is reflected.

6 The reflected beam passes through the mirror.

7 The second lens focuses the reflected beam on to the photodiode.

Photodiode ON

Lasers are used to 'read' the pattern of pits on the CD, so that the recorded sounds can be reproduced.

Getting the quality

Any recording always includes some 'noise' – unwanted extra sound. When you play back an analogue system (LP or tape) you get the noise as well as the original sound.

CDs also have 'noise' – the surface is not perfectly smooth – but at playback, each 'bit' is read either as 1 or 0. There can't be any other numbers, so any small amounts of 'noise' are simply ignored by the laser reader, and do not feature in the playback.

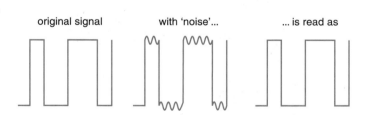

original signal   with 'noise'...   ... is read as

Noise is ignored when reading a digital recording, so the sound reproduction seems much clearer.

Digital phones

Your digital phone samples your voice and transmits it as bits of digital information on a low power microwave. The quality is better than for earlier analogue phones because the digital transmission and detection system means noise is eliminated, as it is in the CD player.

The *range* of accurate transmission of the signal is limited, however, so microwave repeater masts are seen in most parts of the country.

1 The diagrams show light reaching a prism in some pieces of optical equipment. Copy the diagrams carefully and use a pencil and ruler to draw the path of the light through each one.

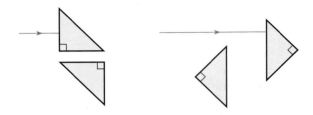

2 There are two main types of lenses. Which type always produces the same sort of image no matter where the object is placed? Describe what you would see happen to the image of an object that starts close to a magnifying glass and is then steadily moved away from it.

3 Think carefully about the camera and the eye and then write down three similarities and two differences between them.

4 Red light of wavelength 6×10^{-10} m is travelling through air at 3×10^8 m/s. What is its frequency?

5 A microwave oven uses electromagnetic waves of wavelength 12 cm (0.12 m) and frequency 2500 MHz. What is the speed of the waves?

6 An ultrasound transmitter in a hospital uses sound waves with a frequency of 3 MHz and wavelength of 0.11mm. What is the speed of the waves?
   The waves from an ultrasound scanner pass through small gaps between parts of the body. Why is it important that the wavelength of the waves is small?
   What is the advantage of using ultrasound when compared with X-rays?

7 John's house is only about 30 km from a radio station that transmits his favourite programme on both FM at 90 MHz (3.3 m wavelength) and Long Wave 200 kHz (1500 m wavelength). He can receive the Long wave transmission quite clearly but not the FM. He thinks that a hill between the house and the transmitter may make a difference. Write a letter to explain the reception problem to him, with a diagram to show what is happening to the waves.

8 Some reporters and businessmen take a small satellite transmitter with them so that they can communicate with home when they are a long way from a telephone line.
   What shape of aerial will they need? Draw it and show how waves will be sent out in a fairly narrow beam to the satellite.
   What sort of waves do you think that they will transmit to the satellite?
   Where will the satellite be? How does this help to get the aerial in roughly the right direction?

9 Jenna is listening to sound coming through a doorway from another room. The sound has a frequency of 680 Hz. If the speed of sound is 340 m/s what is the wavelength of the sound? The doorway is 0.7 m wide. Explain how this makes the sound spread out sideways into Jenna's room

10 In your stereo at home there will be small speakers for high frequencies and big speakers for low frequencies.
   How does this help to spread both sets of frequencies by the same amount so that you hear both clearly?

11 a Radio waves can be reflected off the ionosphere if they are of the right wavelength. In the daytime the layers can be as low as 70 km above the Earth but at night the main reflecting layer is about 300 km above the Earth. What difference does this make to the range of a short wave radio station? Draw a small diagram to help explain what you mean.

   b Microwaves are shorter than the radio waves and are not reflected by the ionosphere. Why does this make them better for satellite communication?

12 Anita is using her computer to record some pieces of music onto a rewritable CD. The program gives her a choice of sampling rate from the microphone input and a choice of 8 bit or 16 bit recording on the CD.
   Explain to her what difference each of the choices will make.

Heinemann Educational Publishers

Halley Court, Jordan Hill, Oxford, OX2 8EJ

a division of Reed Educational & Professional Publishing Ltd

Heinemann is a registered trademark of Reed Educational & Professional Publishing Ltd

OXFORD MELBOURNE AUCKLAND

JOHANNESBURG BLANTYRE GABORONE

IBADAN PORTSMOUTH NH (USA) CHICAGO

© University of York Science Education Group, 2001

First published 2001

ISBN 0 435 62952 2

05 04 03 02 01

10 9 8 7 6 5 4 3 2 1

Writing team for revision of the Unit Guides

Gill Alderton, Michael Brimicombe, Byron Dawson, Bob McDuell, Keith Palfreyman and Ann Tiernan

Salters and Heinemann would also like to thank anyone else involved in the project.

Project directed by Peter Nicolson

Edited by Alexandra Clayton and Gina Walker

Index compiled by Diana Boatman

Designed and typeset by Cambridge Publishing Management Ltd

Illustrated by Hardlines Ltd

Printed and bound in Great Britain by Bath Colourbooks, Glasgow

Acknowledgements

The authors and publishers would like to thank the following for permission to use photographs: **p3** Still Pictures/Daniel Dancer; **p4** Andrew Lambert; **p11** Corbis/James L. Amos; **p12** Science Photo Library/Alex Bartel; **p17** St. Bartholemew's Hospital; **p20** Science Photo Library/Francis Leroy; **p25** Science Photo Library/Simon Fraser; **p26** Science Photo Library/J.C. Revy; **p28** *MR* Science Photo Library/USDA, *BR* Science Photo Library/Chris Priest; **p29** *TR* Science Photo Library/Quest, *MR* Science Photo Library/Sinclair Stammers, *BR* Science Photo Library/Manfred Kaye; **p32** Andrew Lambert; **p37** The Salt Union; **p42** *TR* Mary Evans Picture Library, *BR* Royal Society of Chemistry; **p43** Ann Ronan Picture Library; **p47** Andrew Lambert; **p48** Trevor Hill; **p52** Peter Morris; **p54** *MR* Photodisc 57167.jpg, *BR* Peter Gould; **p60** *TL* Andrew Lambert, *MR* Environmental Images; **p61** Empics/Jed Leicester; **p62** *BM* MG Rover Group, *BR* Land Rover; **p63** *TR* Robert Harding Picture Library/Tony Gervis, *MR* T. Hill, *BR* Andrew Lambert; **p64** Empics/Jon Buckle; **p67** Genesis Space Photo Library/Spaceport; **p70** Peter Gould; **p72** Peugeot; **p73** *TR* MIRA, *BR* Action-Plus Photographic/Steve Bardens; **p77** (main) Still Pictures/Mark Edwards, (inset) Panos Pictures/Liba Taylor; **p89** Holt Studios/Nigel Cattlin; **p90** *TM* Science Photo Library/Astrid and Hanns-Frieder Michler, *TR* Andrew Lambert, *MR* Science Photo Library/Ken Eward; **p91** Andrew Lambert; **p92** *TR* Science Photo Library/David Scharf, *BR* Robert Harding; **p98** Photodisc 34095.jpg; **p101** Geoscience Features Picture Library; **p104** Geoscience Features Picture Library; **p105** Associated Press **p106**; Mary Evans Picture Library; **p109** Science Picture Library/Dr Morley Read; **p110** *TL* Bruce Coleman Collection/Pacific Stock, *TR* Geoscience Features, *ML* NHPA/Trevor McDonald, *MR* Geoscience Features, *BL* Corbis, *BR* Geoscience Features Picture Library; **p112** (all three) Geoscience Features Picture Library; **p113** Trevor Hill; **p117** *TR* Mark Wagner, *BR* Andrew Lambert; **p118** Trevor Hill; **p121** Science Photo Library/Tek Image; **p124** Trevor Hill; **p125** *TR* Gareth Boden, *MR* Science Photo Library/Sheila Terry, *BR* Science Photo Library/Sheila Terry; **p128** Trevor Hill; **p129** Science Photo Library/Martin Bond; **p130** *TL* Natural History Museum, *TR* Natural History Museum, *ML* GSF Picture Library, *MR* GSF Picture Library/Dr B. Booth, *BL* Natural History Museum, *BR* Natural History Museum; **p131** Milepost 92½; **p132** Holt Studios; **p136** Britstock-IFA/T.P.L.; **p137** Science Photo Library/Rosenfeld Images; **p138** Milepost 92½; **p142** Panos Pictures/Howard Davies; **p143** Anglesey Aluminium Metal Ltd.; **p147** *L* Still Pictures/Francois Pierrel, *R* Still Pictures/Mike Kolloffel; **p148** Bruce Coleman Collection/Jane Burton; **p150** *TR* Science Photo Library/Nigel Dennis, *BR* Mary Evans Picture Library; **p152** *TR* Bruce Coleman Collection/Colin Varndell, *TMR* Bruce Coleman Collection/Sir Jeremy Grayson, *BMR* NHPA/A.P. Barnes, *BR* Bruce Coleman Collection/Roine Magnusson; **p160** *TR* Mary Evans Picture Library, *MR* Holt Studios/Gordon Roberts; **p161** *BR* Holt Studios/Peter Wilson, *MR* Holt Studios/Inga Spence; **p165** *L* Science Photo Library/Martin Dohr, *R* Science Photo Library/Martin Bond; **p166** *TR* Sally & Richard Greenhill, *BR* Science Photo Library/Adam Hart-Davies; **p171** Trevor Hill **p172** Trevor Hill; **p173** *TR* Trevor Hill, *BR* Vodaphone; **p175** Trevor Hill; **p176** Science Photo Library/Sue Ford; **p177** Mary Evans Picture Library; **p180** Trevor Hill; **p181** Science Photo Library/Dr Jeremy Burgess.

Cover photo by Science Photo Library/Hugh Turvey

Picture research by Jennifer Johnson